A.G.G.R.E.G.T.E.

BOOK 1

-JIM KRUEGER

WRITER -- JUSTICE, EARTH X, FOOT SOLDIERS,
THE HIGH COST OF HAPPILY EVER AFTER, THE RUNNER & MUCH MORE.

MAYBE YOU SHOULD READ THIS AFTER YOUR FIRST READ OF THE BOOK...
OR MAYBE YOU SHOULD READ IT AFTER YOUR SECOND FIRST READ OF THE BOOK...
OR MAYBE YOUR THIRD...

ALRIGHT, YOU CAN READ IT NOW.

If you're like me, your bookshelf is overstocked with Graphic Novels. I like Marvel Masterworks, so that's 250 Books already. And that doesn't include any of the amazing works by the likes of Frank Miller, or Ala[n] Moore, or 70s Kirby, or Jason Aaron, or Grant Morrison, or James Robinson or... and the list goes on... as does my Bookshelf.

Anyhow, I'm at the point where I have to limit things on my bookshelf to these three categories. One, it's somehow research for other projects, and therefore a necessity to hold on to. Two, it inspired me as a kid. And finally, three, it's a book that I will read again.

And it's this third criteria that brings me (and you) to the book you have in your hands... or the book on th[e] tablet that you hold in your hands.

This is the very first SPLIT DECISION comic book. There isn't one story here, there are many. And you, t[he] reader, get to choose where the characters within go on their journey. Not all of them are happy endings. But every choice leads you to a new experience of the book.

Hence, a book that I will read again. And Again. And again. Even if it's only to read it for the first time.

It's sci-fi, it's fantasy, it's post apocalyptic action and thankfully, it's a world I want to spend time in.

Now let me talk about Ben Bishop. I love Ben's art. I love that it's this indy-style that seems to mesh the best of what's in comics today. I see all the things I love about the fusion of both animation and realism in Ben's work.

But more than this, I love how Ben crafts a panel and embraces story-telling. I look at Ben's art and it's li[ke] reading a movie. We've collaborated in the past, and what strikes me first is Ben's ability to tell a story. H[e] approaches the page like a director approaches film. And having written both film and comics, I know that [in] printed sequentials, the writer and artist share the role of director.

There's something very cinematic about what Ben does with a page that makes me want to both study the panel, but move on to see what he's going to do next.

This project is a SPLIT DECISION comic. But there is no split decision for me. I'm all in. And once you g[et] past this intro, so will you be.

I help a lot of writers get their starts. I've given a lot of people notes over the years. There's always one note that I end up giving to everyone. It regards structure. A lot of writers want to just start writing and see where the stories go and where the characters take things. The problem with writing like this (though a short-term study, it can be helpful), is that the project never gets finished.

If you want to write, but haven't started yet, this book might be especially insightful for you as you make decisions throughout.

And along the way, you'll probably land on your favorite story.

I know I have. And it all begins with my friend Ben Bishop.

- Jim

BEN BISHOP WORDS, PICTURES & LETTERS - **BRITTANY PEER** COLORS - **RYAN WING** EDITS

THE AGGREGATE BOOK ONE. FIRST PRINTING. APRIL 2017. COPYRIGHT © 2017 BEN BISHOP. ALL RIGHTS RESERVED. PUBLISHED BY BEN BISHOP PORTLAND MAINE 04101.
THE AGGREGATE ™ AND SPLIT DECISION COMICS™ (INCLUDING ALL PROMINENT CHARACTERS FEATURED HEREIN), ALL LOGOS AND ALL CHARACTERS LIKENESSES ARE TRADEMARKS OF BEN BISHOP, UNLESS OTHERWISE NOTED.
ALL RIGHTS RESERVED. NO PART OF THIS PUBLICATION MAY BE REPRODUCED OR TRANSMITTED, IN ANY FORM OR BY ANY MEANS (EXCEPT FOR SHORT EXCERPTS FOR JOURNALISTIC OR REVIEW PURPOSES) WITHOUT THE EXPRESS
PERMISSION OF BEN BISHOP. ALL NAMES, CHARACTERS, EVENTS AND LOCALES IN THIS PUBLICATION ARE ENTIRELY FICTIONAL. ANY RESEMBLANCE TO ACTUAL PERSONS (LIVING OR DEAD), EVENTS OR PLACES, WITHOUT SATIRIC IN
COINCIDENTAL. PRINTED IN CANADA. FOR ADITIONAL INFORMATION REGARDING RIGHTS AND USAGE CONTACT BEN BISHOP. BEN.BISHART@GMAIL.COM / WWW.BISHART.NET / OR ON TWITTER AND INSTAGRAM @BISHART
ISBN: 978-0-692-86528-6

WWW.BISHART.NET - WWW.THEAGGREGATEBOOK.COM - WWW.SPLITDECISIONCOMICS.COM
- @BISHART - @THEAGGREGATEBOOK

THIS IS NO ORDINARY COMIC...

THIS IS A **SPLIT DECISION COMIC!**

THAT MEANS **YOU** ARE IN CHARGE OF THE CHARACTERS' DECISIONS, RESPONSES, ACTIONS AND SOMETIMES EVEN THEIR **DEATHS!** ULTIMATELY **YOU** ARE IN CONTROL OF WHERE THE ENTIRE STORY GOES, FOR **BETTER** OR **WORSE!**

THERE ARE MANY DIFFERENT **SPLIT DECISION** STORY THREADS WITHIN **THE AGGREGATE** WORLD AND EACH ONE WILL GIVE YOU A DIFFERENT POINT OF VIEW OR PERSPECTIVE ON ANY GIVEN SITUATION BASED ON **YOUR DECISIONS!**

KEEP AN EYE OUT FOR **SPLIT DECISIONS** LIKE **THESE** AT THE BOTTOM OF THE PAGE...

STAY - PAGE **54**

AND PEEK CAREFULLY FOR THE PAGE NUMBER IN THE TOP PAGE CORNERS TO FIND YOUR **DESTINATION.**

IF YOU DON'T SEE A **SPLIT DECISION** OPTION, YOU JUST KEEP READING LIKE A **NORMAL** COMIC.

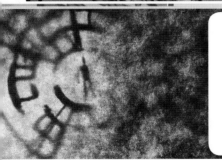

THROUGHOUT THIS BOOK, YOU'LL ALSO COME ACROSS PAGES LIKE **THESE!**

DON'T WORRY, THE STORY ISN'T OVER, THESE ARE **SPLIT DECISION** SPOILER SHIELDS. YOU WOULDN'T WANT TO KNOW WHAT FATE HAS IN STORE FOR YOU BEFORE **DECIDING** FOR YOURSELF WOULD YOU?

IN **THE AGGREGATE** YOU'LL BE TASKED WITH MAKING **DECISIONS** FOR SEVERAL DIFFERENT CHARACTERS SO CHOOSE WISELY... OR ELSE...

JUST KIDDING, IT'S NOT ACTUALLY **THE END OF THE WORLD.** YOU CAN ALWAYS BACKTRACK TO YOUR LAST **SPLIT DECISION** (LET'S BE HONEST, YOU'RE PROBABLY GOING TO **CHEAT** AREN'T YOU?) **OR** YOU CAN START BACK AT PAGE 1 AND EXPERIENCE **THE AGGREGATE** BOOK ALL OVER AGAIN IN AN ALL NEW WAY WITH EACH AND EVERY READ, CRAFTING **YOUR OWN** PERSONALIZED ADVENTURE!

BEN BISHOP

SPLIT DECISION COMICS

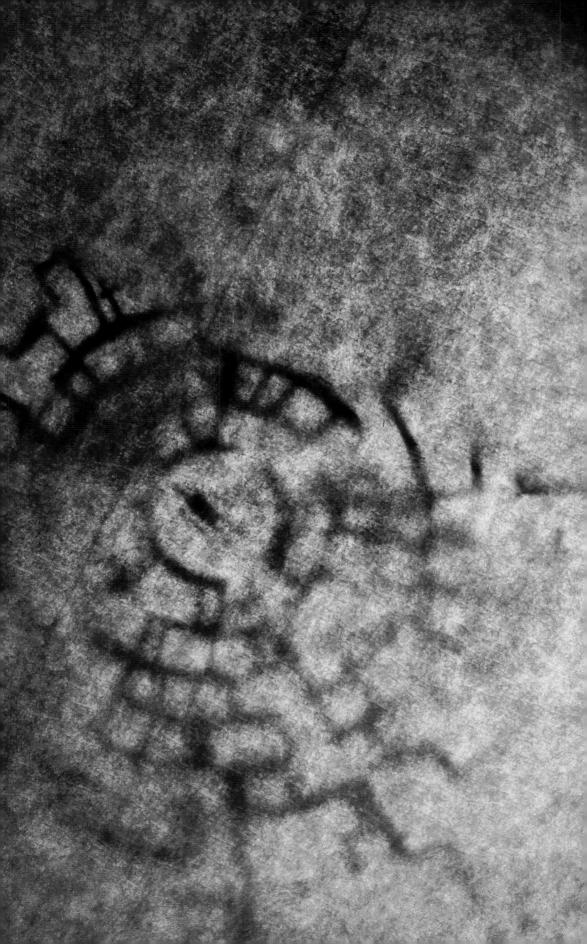

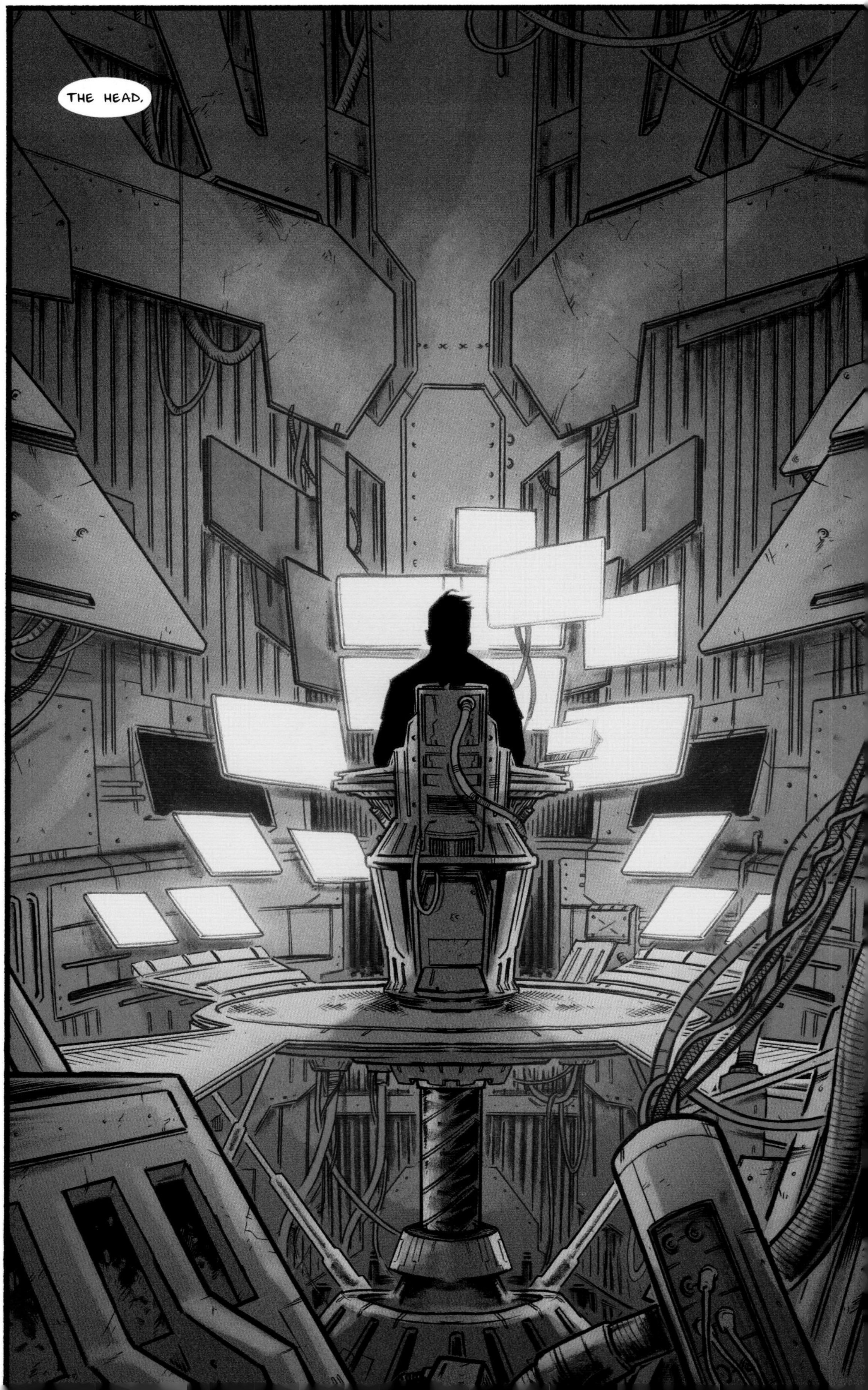
THE HEAD.

WHAT IN GOD'S NAME WAS THA--
SKRASH
WE'RE TOO LATE.
WHAT!? WE'VE GOT THEM ON THE ROPES. WHAT ARE YOU--
VAL...
THIS IS ALL OUR FAULT.

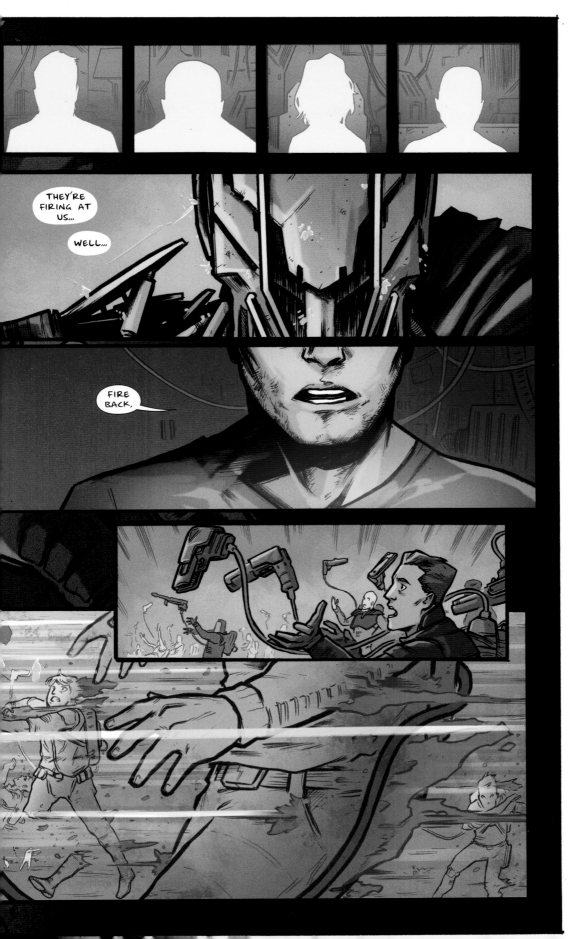

VAL?

YOU ALRIGHT?

YOU DON'T HAVE TO DO THIS...

YOU DON'T HAVE TO DO THIS...

AND WHAT? TRUST YOU TO SAVE THE WORLD ALL BY YOURSELF?

NOT IN A THOUSAND YEARS.

A.G.G.R.E.G.A.T.E

A SPLIT DECISION COMIC. BY BEN BISHOP WITH COLORS BY BRITTANY PEER

6 MONTHS AFTER THE AGGREGATE.

THAT'S THE FOURTH TIME THIS MORNING.

THIS NEIGHBORHOOD'S GOING TO HELL, I'LL TELL YOU WHAT.

HASN'T BEEN A SINGLE FOOD AND WATER DROP OFF IN 2 MONTHS NOW, CAN YOU BLAME PEOPLE FOR KEELING OVER?

MARCHAN BANNISTER OF THE NEW BRIDGE MET WITH THE HIGH COUNCIL ON SUNDAY TO DISCUSS THE NEW BILL OUTLAWING SALE AND DISTRIBUTION OF PRECIOUS OILS. WHEN ASKED BY CENTER 66 HOW THE **NEW BRIDGE** EXPECTS THE PEOPLE OF EARTH TO GO ABOUT THEIR LIVES IN A WORLD WITHOUT TRANSPORTATION HE SIMPLY **SHRUGGED.**

PUTZ. BUNCH O SECOND A THIRD RA MORONS.

...AT LEAST THOSE OLD FOOLS WERE WORKING ON SOME KIND OF PLAN.

THEY KNEW THE WORLD WAS GETTING TOO BIG FOR IT'S BRITCHES AND WOULD HAVE FOUND A WAY TO FIX IT...

...SEND US TO POPULATE SOME NEW PLANET OR SOMETHING...

OR SOMETHING.

WHAT A WASTE...

IS SHE WOUNDED?

SHE HASN'T EATEN IN EIGHT NIGHTS.

HOW IS THAT POSSIBLE?

WHAT DO WE DO WITH HER?

WHAT WE MUST...

...TO PROTECT THEM.

SHOOOOO

HER SCARS....

IS

A MAP?!

ENOUGH!

1 HOUR AFTER THE AGGREGATE.

MAKE SURE YOU FRY **EVERYTHING!**

LAST THING WE NEED IS SOMEONE PICKING UP WHERE **THE BRIDGE** LEFT OFF.

YOU HEARD THE BOSS MAN, LET'S **LIGHT** IT UP!

HOW ABOUT THEM **SUPER FRIENDS?** I'VE GOT ENOUGH IN MY TANK FOR ALL 5 OF THOSE **FREAKS.**

NO! LISTEN UP!

YOU **GOTTA** BE KIDDING ME--

IT'S ALRIGHT, GIVE HER A MINUTE.

THE OTAS ARE NOT TO BE HARMED!

SHE'S JOKING, RIGHT, BOSS?

ENOUGH PEOPLE HAVE DIED TODAY... ON BOTH SIDES.

EVERY ONE OF THOSE PEOPLE DIED BECAUSE THEY **HAD** TO... THEY MADE A CHOICE, THEY KNEW THE RISK. THE OTAS DIDN'T **CHOOSE** ANY OF THIS... TH WERE **CHOSEN.** T DON'T HAVE TO D FOR US TO LIVE

THAT'S WHAT SEPERATES **US** FROM THE PEOPLE THAT BUILT THIS THING.

IF WE MURDER THE OTAs AS SOME KIND OF PREEMPTIVE MEASURE AGAINST A POTENTIAL FUTURE THREAT THAT MAY OR MAY NOT EVEN EXIST...

WELL THEN WE'RE JUST AS BAD AS THEM.

THE BRIDGE WANTED TO USE THE OTAs AND THEIR WEAPON AS A WAY TO WIPE THE SLATE CLEAN...

WE HAVE A FRESH START NOW. A CHANCE TO BE THE PEOPLE WE WANT TO BE...

LOOK, IF YOU ALL WANT TO CONTINUE TO BE KNOWN AS CRIMINALS AND MURDERERS HIDING BENEATH THE STREETS...

BUT, IF THE LIGHT IS REALLY ALL YOU SAY IT IS... "A SHINING BEACON, A BETTER FUTURE"...

LET TODAY BE THE FIRST DAY OF THAT FUTURE.

THE CHOICES WE MAKE TODAY HAVE THE POWER TO LITERALLY CHANGE THE WORLD AROUND US.

SHE'S RIGHT.

WHAT?!

WHAT?

WE'RE GOING TO **BURY** THIS PLACE IN THE EARTH, ALONG WITH THE **ROBOT** AND ANY R&D THEY'VE GOT. THIS PLACE WILL HAVE **NEVER** HAVE EXISTED...

BUT THE OTAs WILL BE SPARED.

WHAT DO YOU SUGGEST **BOSS?**

I... UH. WELL, WE'LL NEED TO KEEP THEM AS FAR FROM EACH OTHER AS POSSIBLE... AS LONG AS THEY'RE ASLEEP THERE'S NOTHING TO WORRY ABOUT, SHOULD THEY WAKE UP, IT'S PROBABLY BEST TO KEEP THEM SEPARATED, FOR NOW...

ABSOLUTELY, I WANT THEM UNDER CONSTANT SURVEILLANCE, THEY COULD WAKE UP ANY TIME NOW AND WE DON'T KNOW WHAT TO EXPECT.

KEEP THEM SEPARATED, KEEP THEM SAFE... THAT'S AN ORDER.

AND THEN **WHAT?!** WHAT HAPPENS WHEN THEY **DO** WAKE UP?!

WELL, I GUESS WE'LL DEAL WITH THAT WHEN IT NEEDS DEALING WITH.

THIS IS BULLSHIT.

I HAVE TO GO NOW...

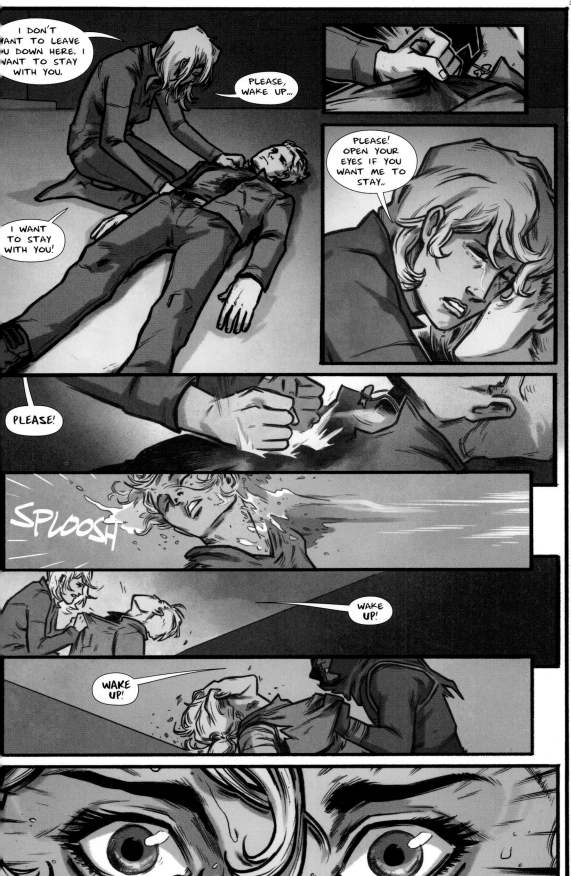

1000 YEARS AFTER THE AGGREGATE.

THERE YOU ARE...

ASK HER WHY SHE'S GOT A MAP CARVED INTO HER STOMACH...

BETTER YET, WHY THERE'S A BLOODY FRESH CIRCLE RIGHT AROUND OUR VERY LOCATION?

BACK OFF DIEGUES!

RADEK WILL FIND OUT EVERYTHING WE NEED TO KNOW... ONE WAY OR ANOTHER.

CALM DOWN!

GUYS!

ENOUGH.

EVERYONE OUT.

HI.

MEMBER ME?

I DON'T KNOW WHY I'M STILL ALIVE, MAYBE IT'S SOME KIND OF TWISTED **JUSTICE**.

SOME KIND OF **JOKE**.

FROM SOME KIND OF CRUEL **GOD**...

EAH... GOD."

A PUNISHMENT I MUST DESERVE...

TO WATCH EVERYONE AROUND ME DIE.

WHILE DAY AFTER DAY, I GO ON BREATHING...

I DON'T AGE, MY BONES DON'T ACHE...

I DON'T DIE.

HELL, I'M NOT EVEN HUNGRY ANYMORE.

FOR A LONG TIME, THERE WAS NOTHING TO EAT ANYWAY...

THAT'S WHEN I SET MY RECORD.

10,674 DAYS WITHOUT FOOD, DOESN'T SEEM **THAT** LONG, ALL THINGS CONSIDERED.

IT WASN'T UNTIL, AFTER DECADES OF ASH, I SAW A SINGLE APPLE ON THE BRANCH OF A TREE...

COULDN'T HELP IT...

WONDER HOW LONG I COULD HAVE GONE, HAD IT NOT BEEN FOR THAT **APPLE**?

I GUESS YOU'VE GOT ME BEAT THOUGH... YOU HAVEN'T EVEN TAKEN A **PISS** IN 1000 YEARS.

WHEN I SAW THAT APPLE, ALL I COULD THINK ABOUT WAS **SNOW WHITE**.

WEIRD THING TO THINK ABOUT AFTER ALL I'VE SEEN BUT--

I THOUGHT TO MYSELF... MAYBE IT'S A TRICK?

I THOUGHT, WHAT IF IT'S POISONOUS LIKE IN THE STORY, AND I FALL ASLEEP AND CAN'T WAKE UP?

THAT'S WHY I BIT INTO THE **APPLE**...

NOT BECAUSE I WAS **HUNGRY**, BECAUSE I WANTED TO GO TO **SLEEP**...

I WANTED TO **DIE**.

NO SUCH **LUCK**...

YOU SEE, WHILE YOU'VE BEEN SLEEPING, I'VE BEEN ADAPTING... *SURVIVING.*

AND I'VE LEARNED A LOT.

IMAGINE THE LIFETIME OF A PAINTER, THIER PROGRESS AND IMPROVEMENT OVER TIME WITH PRACTICE.

HOW SKILLED WOULD THEY BE AT AGE 30? AGE 60?

WHAT ABOUT 1,000?

HOW GOOD A PAINTER WOULD THEY WOULD BE AFTER PRACTICING THEIR CRAFT FOR 1000 YEARS?

PRETTY *DAMN GOOD.*

YOU'RE NOT SUPPOSED TO BE IN HERE YOU KNOW...

I WAS JUST LEAVING...

OH, NO, PLEASE, DON'T MIND ME, CONTINUE...

WHAT IS IT ABOUT HIM?

RADEK, YOU'RE DRUNK, YOU'RE GOING TO HURT YOURSELF WITH THAT.

EXCUSE ME?

I DON'T EQUATE ONE'S FAILURE TO DIE AS GODLINESS... NOR DO I BELIEVE YOUR FONDNESS FOR HIM IS THAT OF WORSHIP...

HIM, EVERY ONE OF YOU PEOPLE WORSHIP HIM... LOVE HIM...

YOU DON'T WORSHIP THE OTAs AS THE REST OF YOUR PEOPLE DO?

SO WHAT THEN?

KILL ME WITH A BROKEN BOTTLE?

THIS IS RIDICULOUS, GET--

I'M NOT HERE FOR YOU!

AS A MEMBER OF THE LIGHT, WE'RE SWORN TO PROTECT THE OTAs AT ALL COST AGAINST ANY WHO WOULD DO THEM HARM...

AH, THE CREED...

LET'S SEE WHAT SORT OF GOD CAN BE KILLED IN HIS SLEEP!

YOU-- **YOU CUT THEM CLEAN OFF**...

I DID, SHALL I CONTINUE?

CLAIMING YOU SLIT YOUR OWN THROAT WHEN YOU DRUNKENLY TRIPPED AND FELL ON YOUR OWN WINE GLASS WON'T BE AN EASY TALE TO TELL...

BUT I'M A **DAMN** GOOD STORYTELLER...

I'VE HAD **MANY** YEARS OF PRACTICE, MANY, MANY YEARS.

NOW, GET UP, TURN AROUND, WALK OUT OF HERE AND I WILL TELL NO ONE WHAT YOU **ATTEMPTED** TO DO HERE TONIGHT.

FOR THEY WILL **SURELY KILL YOU** FOR IT.

WHO ARE YOU?

TURN TO - PAGE **68**

TURN TO - PAGE 68

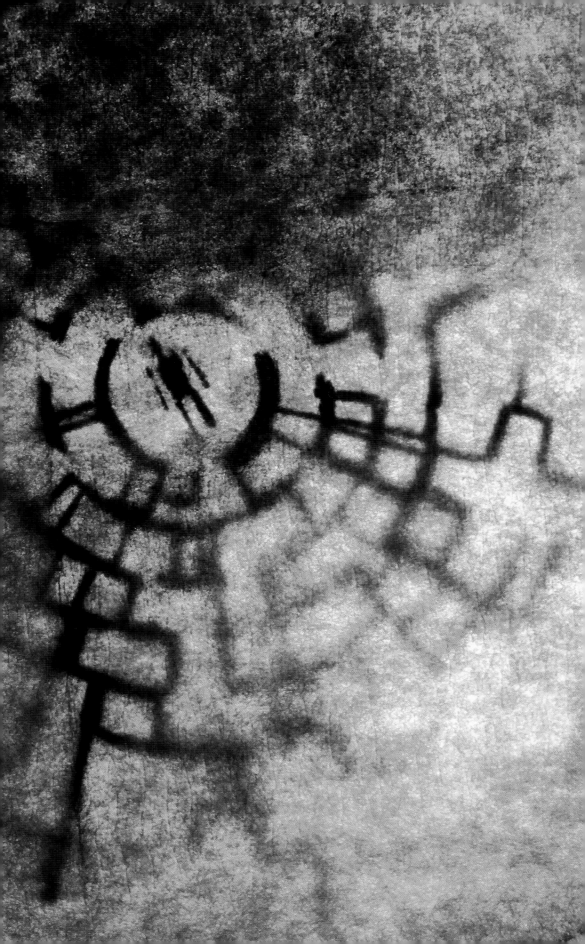

7 HOURS BEFORE THE AGGREGATE.

ARE YOU UP?

YEAH, CAN'T SLEEP. DID I WAKE YOU?

NAH, I'VE BEEN UP A FEW HOURS NOW.

WHAT'S WRONG?

THIS CAN'T BE THE WORST PLACE YOU'VE EVER SPENT THE NIGHT...

WET CONCRETE... SLEEPING BAGS...

NO, YOU'RE RIGHT, THERE WAS PHOENIX. AT LEAST HERE WE HAVE A ROOF OVER OUR HEADS.

WHAT?! ARE YOU KIDDING? I WOULD TAKE THOSE STARS AND WIDE OPEN SPACES OVER ANY BED...

ANY DAY.

YOU SAID YOU LOVED THAT TRIP!

I DID! THOSE WERE THE EARLY DAYS! DIDN'T WANT YOU THINK I COULDN'T ROUGH IT.

I WOULD HAVE SLEPT ON THE GROUND TO GET ON YOUR GOOD SIDE.

ALTHOUGH... THE BED OF YOUR TRUCK WAS BARE A STEP UP FROM THE GROUND.

IT'S LIKE I DON'T EVEN KNOW YOU ANYMORE.

OH, COME ON! YOU'RE TELLING ME YOU THOUGHT THAT TRUCK WAS COMFORTABLE?

I LOVED THAT TRUCK...

THAT WAS A GOOD TRIP.

IT WAS...

WHEN ALL THIS IS OVER, LET'S DO THAT AGAIN.

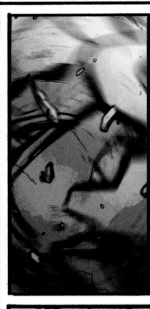
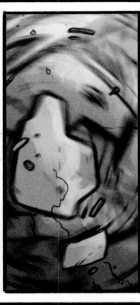

1000 YEARS AFTER THE AGGREGATE.

SNIF SNIF

SNIF

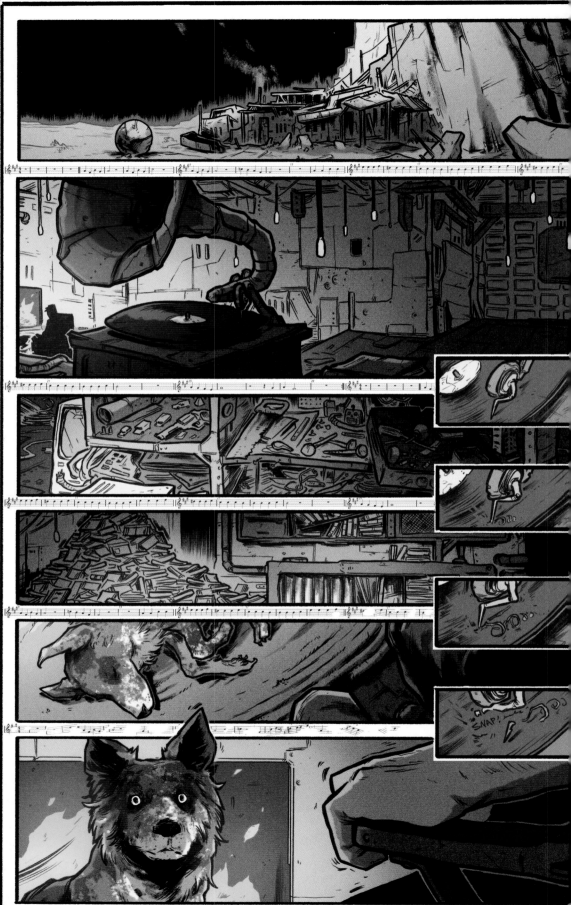

TURN TO - PAGE **68**

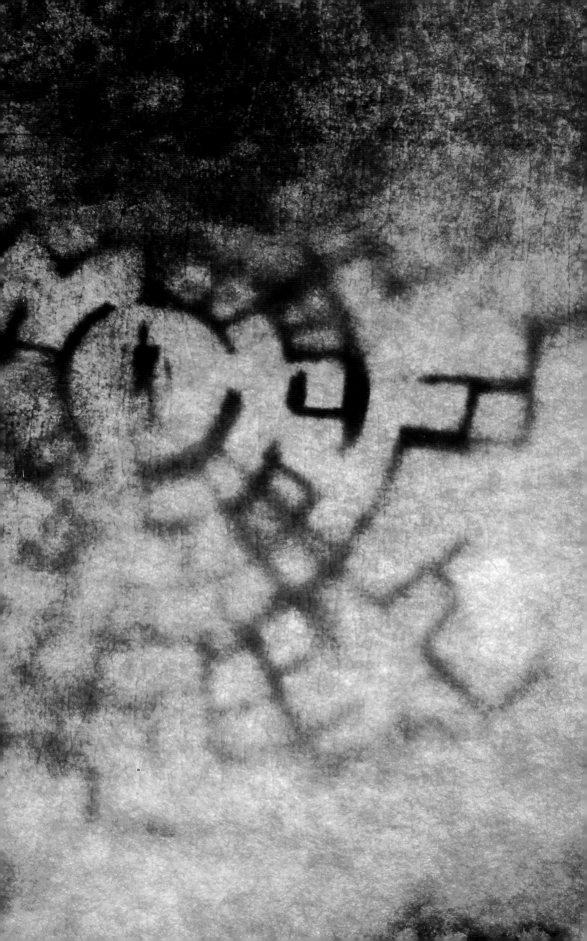

SOME TIME LATER...

THEY WILL [W]EAR THIS WORLD [D]OWN JUST AS IT [I]S BEGUN TO PICK [I]TSELF BACK UP.

WHY WERE YOU MEETING WITH THE COUNCIL?

WE'VE BEEN TRYING, BUT HAVE BEEN UNABLE TO REACH ANY OF THE OTHER LIGHT POSTS.

EVERY MESSENGER WE SEND... NOTHING.

WE'RE LEFT TO [A]SSUME THE WORST.

THEY'RE [A]LL AWAKE NOW...

THE COUNCIL HAS AGREED TO MY DECISION...

IN LIGHT OF LAST NIGHT'S...

TRAGEDY.

WHAT TRAGEDY?

AS SOON AS I HEARD — I HAD TO GET ARIC OUT OF HERE AND YOU AWAY FROM THAT OTA.

HIS BOY IS WITH MZ. K NOW, SAFE. I-- I STILL DON'T KNOW HOW TO TELL THEM.

TELL THEM WHAT?

LAST NIGHT, WHILE YOU WERE SUPPOSED TO BE WATCHING HIM, THE OTA CREPT IN AND MURDERED ARIC'S WIFE AND DAUGHTERS.

THAT'S NOT POSSIBLE. LAST NIGHT THE MAN WAS IN HIS SHACK. I SAW HIM GO IN AND I SAW HIM COME OUT THIS MORNING.

YOU SEE WHAT HE WANTS YOU TO SEE.

I'M SORRY MY LOVE, BUT YOU'VE MADE YOUR DECISION...

TO BETRAY YOUR OWN PEOPLE... FOR THAT THING! YOU BETRAY ME.

I SEE NOW I HAVE BEEN AS BLIND AS YOU, SELFISHLY SEEING ONLY WHAT I WANTED TO BELIEVE IN SO BADLY, RATHER THAN THE TRUTH...

THE TRUTH IS YOU'RE NOT WHO I THOUGHT YOU WERE AND I CAN'T TRUST YOU TO DO WHAT NEEDS TO BE DONE NEXT.

ENSURING OUR OWN BRIGHT FUTURE AND THAT OF THE ENTIRE WORLD, THE COUNCIL HAS AGREED THAT WE MUST KEEP THE OTAS FROM UNITING AT ALL COSTS.

NOW STAY PUT...

FOR YOUR OWN PROTECTION.

RADEK!

WHAT?! THIS IS ABSURD!

LET GO!

YOU CAN'T!

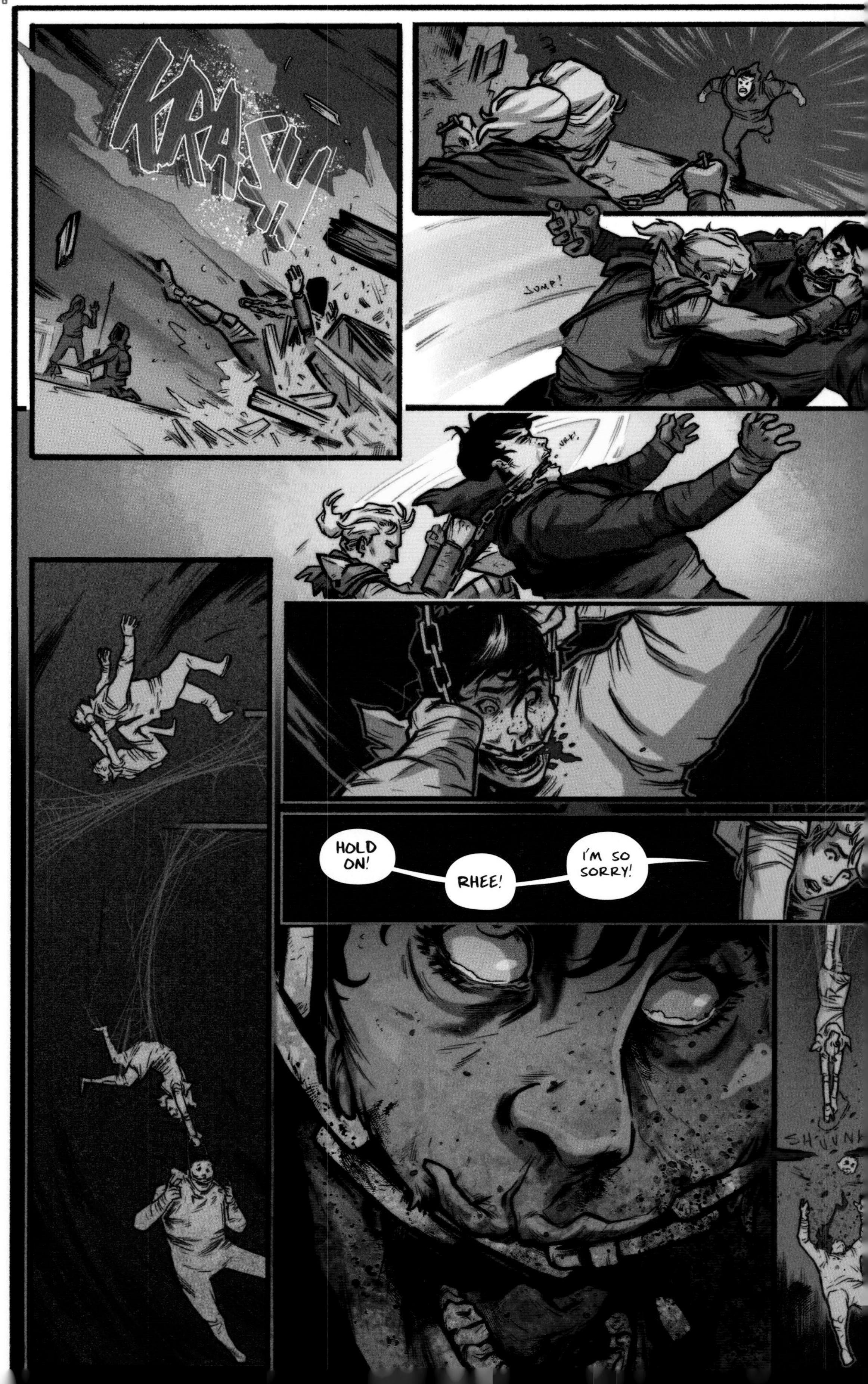
KRASH
JUMP!
URK!
HOLD ON!
RHEE!
I'M SO SORRY!
SHUUNK

CLANG!

WHERE'S MY CAT?!

88

NO...

WHAT HAVE YOU--

YOU KILLED HER!

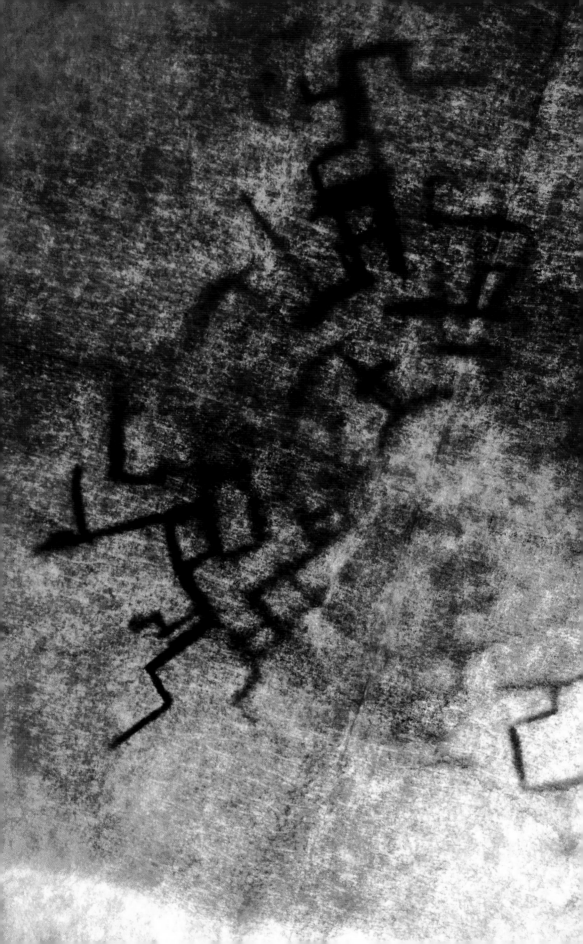

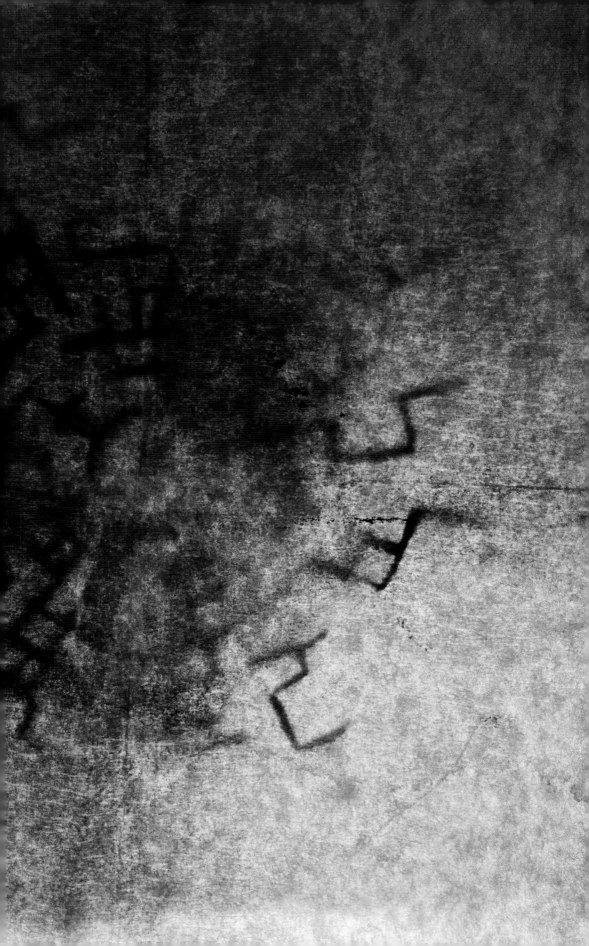

WHEN THEY ATTACKED YOU TODAY, YOU WERE ON YOUR WAY TO SOMETHING...

CORRECT?

TO STOP YOU FROM GETTING THERE...

ARE WE UNDERGROUND?

GRRR

IT'S THE ONLY PLACE I COULD GET AWAY FROM YOUR PEOPLE.

YEAH, THERE'S A REASON FOR THAT, UNCUFF ME! NOW!

LOOK, I'M NOT GOING TO HURT YOU, DON'T YOU THINK YOU COULD STOP ME IF I TRIED?

BARK! BARK! BARK!

YOU NEED TO UNCUFF M RIGHT NOW.

AND WHY IS THAT?

UNCUFF - PAGE **102**

DON'T UNCUFF - PAGE **98**

COME ON!

THANKS.

SHE WILL DRAW THEM CLOSE...

WAIT FOR MY SIGNAL...

CLINK

WAIT!

GO FOR THE EYES.

GO FOR THE EYES...
WAS THAT A JOKE?
SINCE WHEN DO YOU MAKE JOKES?
CRACK
WATCH IT...
HEADS UP!
GOOSH

GO AFTER HER - PAGE 128

LEAVE HER BEHIND - PAGE 108

SIR...

SHOULD I READY THE OTHERS?

NO, LET THEM REST.

WE MAY NOT GET ANOTHER OPPORTUNITY.

LET'S SEE WHERE THEY'RE HEADED, WE MOVE WHEN THEY MOVE.

AND VALERIUS? SHOULDN'T WE RESCUE HER?

DOES SHE LOOK LIKE A PRISONER TO YOU?

SHE'S A TRAITOR... IF SHE GETS IN YOUR WAY...

KILL HER TOO.

IT'S VALERIUS...

BEFORE... YOU ASKED WHO I WAS MY NAME IS VALERIUS. OR VAL....

WHAT ABOUT YOU?

LOOK, WE'VE GOT A LONG WAY TO GO... SHOULD I JUST KEEP CALLING YOU "MAN"?

OR DO YOU HAVE AN ACTUAL NAME?

ALRIGHT. AND YOUR DOG? I SUPPOSE HE'S JUST CALLED "DOG"?

SHE.

WHAT'S THAT?

SHE'S A GIRL.

WELL,

THAT'S A START... GOOD GIRL.

WHY ARE YOU HERE?

GOOD QUESTION...

THOSE PEOPLE I WAS WITH, THEY CALL THEMSELVES **THE LIGHT**, THEY RECENTLY DECIDED THAT YOU ARE A PROBLEM.

THEY WANT TO KILL YOU BEFORE YOU GET WHEREVER IT IS YOU'RE GOING.

BUT **I'M HERE** TO MAKE SURE YOU GET THERE.

AND WHERE IS IT WE'RE GOING?

SHIT, YOU'RE THE ONE LEADING THE WAY, YOU TELL ME.

YESTERDAY YOU MENTIONED **OTHERS**. OTHERS LIKE ME?

YES...

I'VE **SEEN** THEM.

YOU REMEMBER THEM?

NO.

NOT MEMORIES... I CAN'T REMEMBER ANYTHING BEFORE I WOKE UP... JUST FLASHES... HEADACHES... **PAIN.**

IT'S LIKE... WE'RE CONNECTED SOMEHOW.

SOMETIMES, I CAN SEE THEM IN MY **HEAD**... WHAT THEY ARE **DOING**, WHERE THEY ARE **GOING**... I SEE A **MAP**... AND WE'RE ALL HEADED TOWARDS **THE MIDDLE OF IT.**

THE **MAP** YOU DREW IN YOUR SHACK.

WHY GO THERE? TO **THE MIDDLE?**

IMAGINE WAKING UP ONE DAY IN A WORLD YOU DON'T RECOGNIZE...

YOU SPEND EVERY MOMENT LOOKING FOR **SOMETHING,** BUT YOU DON'T KNOW WHAT...

SEARCHING FOR SOME KIND OF REMINDER AS TO WHO YOU **ARE**...

WHO YOU **WERE**... YOU LOOK FOR THAT PURPOSE... BUT YOU ONLY FIND **JUNK.**

THEN ONE NIGHT, THERE'S THIS **FIRE** INSIDE YOUR SKULL AND YOU REALIZE YOU'RE NOT ALONE.

THERE ARE 4 OTHER PEOPLE OUT THERE JUST LIKE YOU...

4 OTHERS WITH THE SAME **PAIN**... AND THE CLOSER WE ALL GET TO EACH OTHER THE LESS IT HURTS.

WHAT WOULD YOU DO?

I SUPPOSE I WOULD WANT TO FIND OUT WHAT IT ALL MEANT.

BUT I'D BE CAUTIOUS...

WELL, THAT'S WHY YOU'RE HERE RIGHT?

TO MAKE SURE NOTHING BAD HAPPENS TO ME...

I SAID I'M GOING TO MAKE SURE YOU GET TO WHERE YOU NEED TO BE...

I NEVER SAID, "**NOTHING** BAD WOULD HAPPEN" WHEN YOU GOT THERE...

SNIF! SNIF!
SNIF!
SNIF! SNIF!

THO...OM

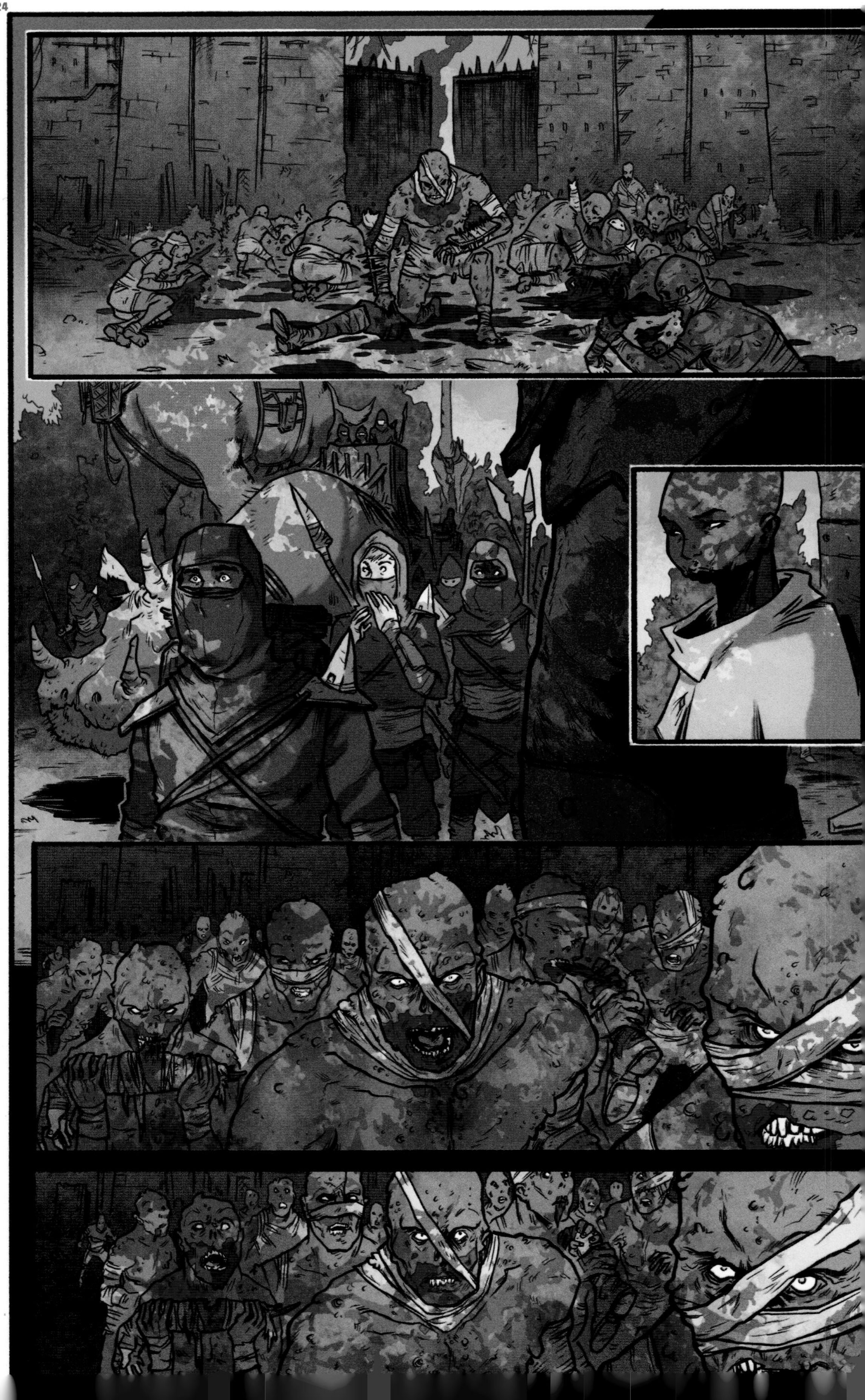

SHUNK

ARE YOU OK?!

YEAH, I'M--

FINE,

WE SHOULD GO, WHAT'S THE PLAN?

METAL STEPS? MAYBE IF YOU WRAPPED SOME PIECES AROUND OUR WAISTS YOU COULD LIFT US--

DOESN'T WORK LIKE THAT...

AND THAT PIECE IS ALL THAT'S LEFT.

PERFECT,

YOU BELIEVE ME?

I'M CHOOSING TO... YEAH.

WHY?

...RADEK'S AN **ASS.** HE'S WANTED YOU **DEAD** FOR A LONG TIME.

AND BECAUSE A LONG TIME AGO **SOMEONE** MADE A CHOICE TO KEEP YOU **SAFE**... AND SOME OF US STILL BELIEVE IN THAT **CHOICE.**

THANK YOU.

TELL YOU WHAT... GET THE THREE OF US OUT OF THIS HOLE **ALIVE** AND WE'LL CALL IT EVEN.

IT'S **VALERIUS** BY THE WAY...

WHAT DO I CALL YOU?

NO ONE'S EVER CALLED ME ANYTHING BEFORE...

WHAT ABOUT UR DOG? HE UST HAVE A NAME?

SHE...

SHE'S A GIRL.

OH... WELL THAT'S A START. **GOOD GIRL.** WE'LL THINK OF **SOMETHING.**

WHAT?

WE'RE COMING UP ON AN OPENING.

I THINK MY EYES ARE ADJUSTING.

HOW DO YOU KNOW WHERE YOU'RE GOING?

I'M NOT SURE EXACTLY. THE **MAP** IN MY HEAD, METALS IN THE EARTH, JUST A **FEELING** I SUPPOSE.

HUH.

DON'T YOU EVER HAVE A FEELING ABOUT SOMETHING?

I DO.

WELL, THAT AND A LACK OF CHOICES...

FROM HERE IT'S EITHER FORWARD OR BACKWARD, AND WE ALREADY KNOW WHAT'S BEHIND US....

I HAVE A PRETTY GOOD IDEA WHAT'S AHEAD OF US AS WELL....

RADEK, HE AND HIS ARMY WILL BE WAITING FOR US.

THEY KNOW WHERE WE'RE HEADED, THEY'VE SEEN THE MAP YOU DREW IN YOUR SHACK...

WE NEED TO FIND YOU SOME SCRAP AND MAKE UP FOR LOST TIME... THE **GOOD** NEWS, IF ANY, IS WE'RE ACTUALLY THE CLOSEST **LIGHT POST** TO **THE MIDDLE**...

THE MIDDLE?

WHAT MAKES YOU THINK THE **OTHERS** ARE HEADED TO THE MIDDLE?

OF THE **MAP**, I'M ASSUMING THAT'S WHERE WE'RE GOING? HOPEFULLY WE'VE GOT A HEAD START OVER THE OTHER **OTA'S**

OTAs?

THAT'S WHAT WE CALL YOU AND THE OTHERS LIKE YOU...

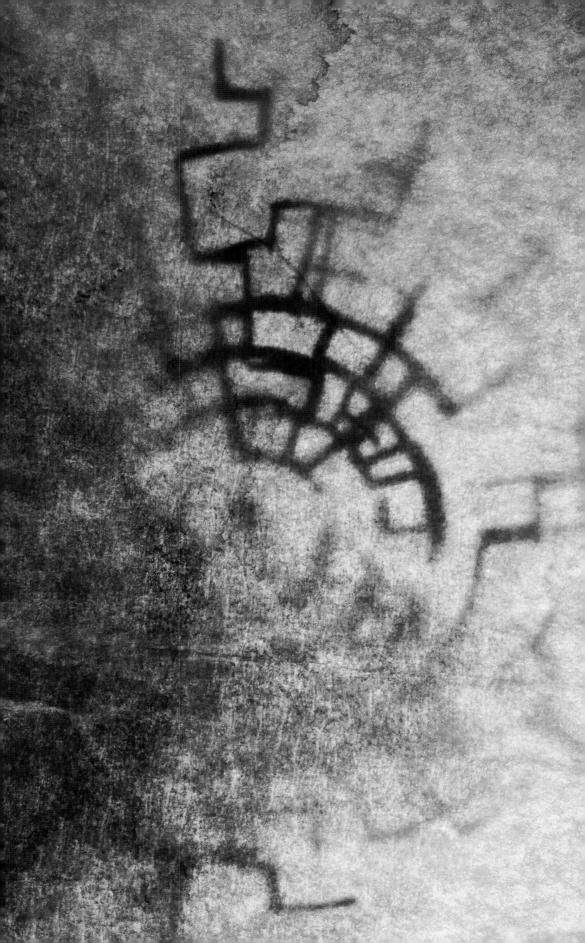

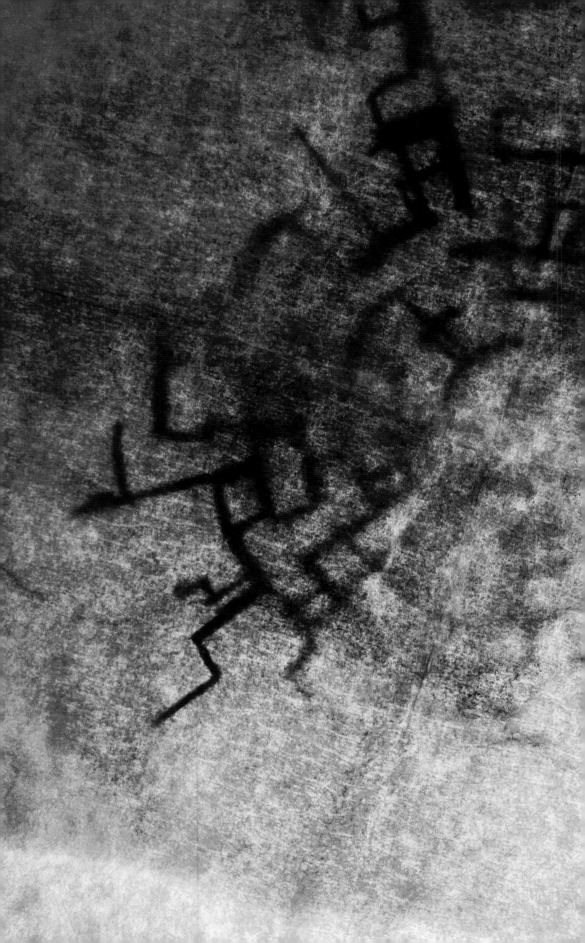

ALL FOUGHT OVER **PRECIOUS** FUELS, ENERGY SOURCES, AND EVENTUALLY EVEN FRESH **WATER**.

YOU'D THINK IF THEY COULD MAKE THEIR **ROBOTS** RUN EXCLUSIVELY ON **SOLAR** THAT THEY COULD FIGURE OUT HOW TO GET BY DAY TO DAY THE SAME WAY...

BUT FOR SOME MEN, THERE'S NO GREATER **POWER SOURCE** THAN THEIR OWN **EGO**... AND THEY JUST WANTED TO **WIN**.

THE COMBINED **GOVERNMENTS** OF THE SURVIVING NATIONS, THE RICHEST THE **RICH**. A COLLECTIVE MASH UP OF UNQUALIFIED MEN AND WOMAN WHO FOUND THEIR WAY TO THE TOP SIMPLY BY THE SIZE OF THEIR WALLETS...

AND THERE WAS **NO ONE** WHO COULD SAY OTHERWISE.

I HAD ALWAYS ASSUMED IT MEANT, "WE **WON**. WE'RE IN CHARGE NOW. SO, BUILD A **BRIDGE** AND GET OVER IT."

"A **BRIDGE** TO **UNIFY** AND **UNITE** THE **WORLD**."

SO, THAT WAS THE END OF THE ROBOT WARS?

THAT WAS THE END OF **EVERYTHING**...

150

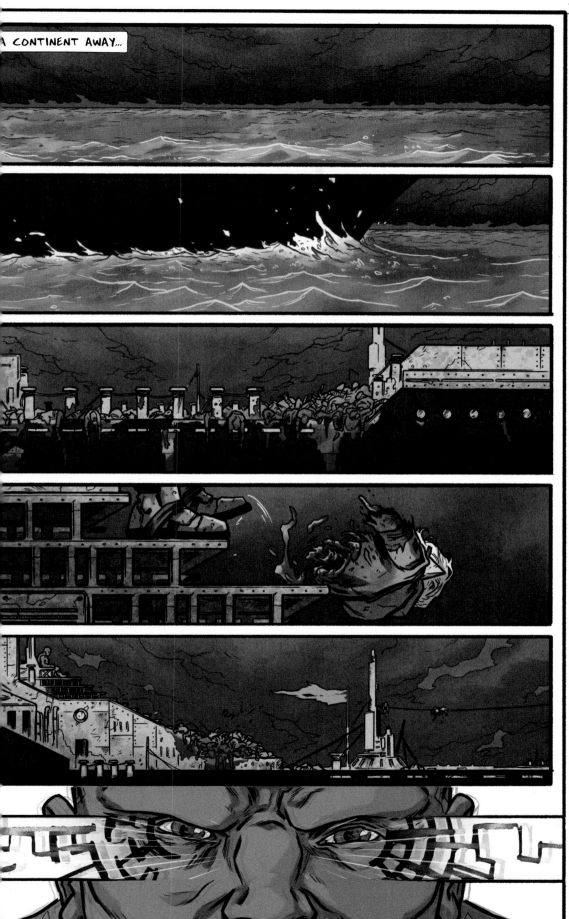

A CONTINENT AWAY...

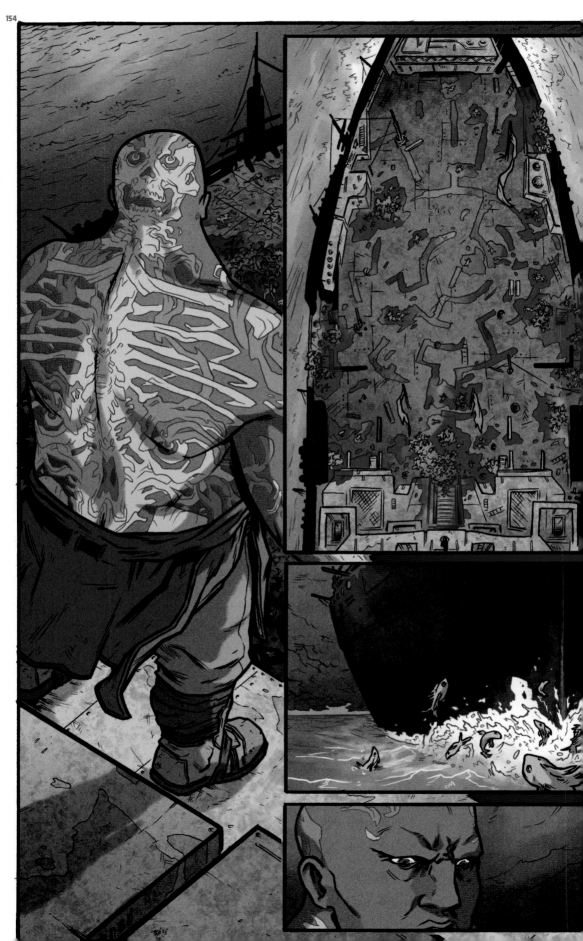

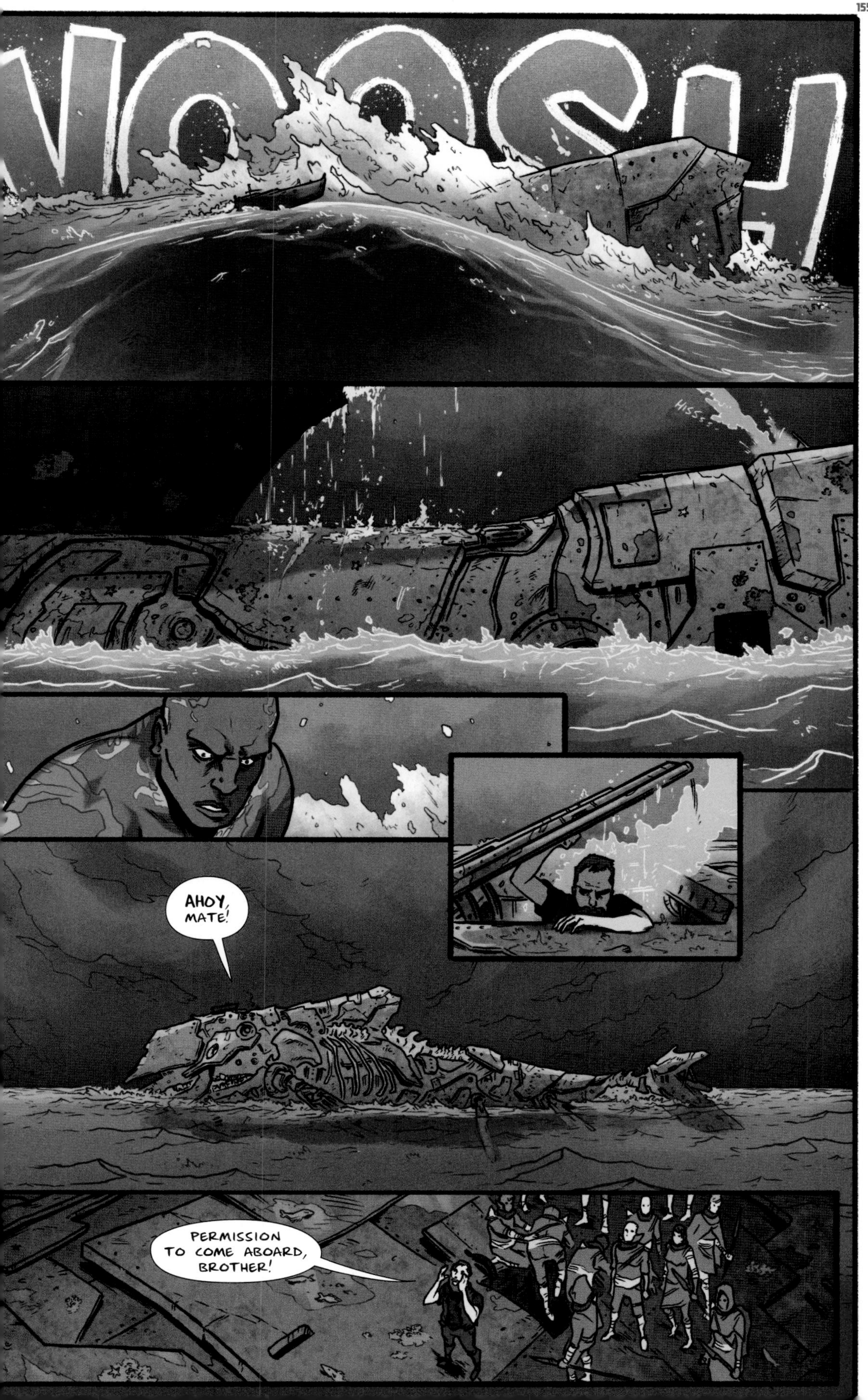
WOOSH
HISS...
AHOY, MATE!
PERMISSION TO COME ABOARD, BROTHER!

AAHH!

GUARDS!

SIR, ARE YOU INJURED?

DO YOU REQUIRE MEDICAL ATTENTION?

HE'S FINE...

SHE BIT ME!

WE'RE FINE, HE'LL LIVE, SHE'S PERFECT, WHO'S NEXT?

THE MALE, GEDEON BOLESLAV.

BOLESLAV?

YEAH, BUT IT SAYS HERE HE GOES BY BRUISER.

OF COURSE HE DOES.

WHAT ELSE?

ANYTHING IN THERE ABOUT BITING PEOPLE?

HILARIOUS... NO, BUT IT DOES SAY HE VERY MUCH DISLIKES BEING TOUCHED.

WHY ON EARTH WOULD I TOUCH HIM, CORGAN?

YOU ASKED ME TO READ THE CHART!

HOLY SHIT!

MAYBE YOU OUGHT TO STAY OUT HERE.

WHAT, WHY? WHAT IS IT?

THIS BLOKE IS HUGE!

BUILT LIKE A BRICK HOUSE WITH A FACE LIKE A BUCKET OF SMASHED CRABS.

WAIT, HE CAN'T HEAR ME CAN HE?

I'M NOT SURE...

1 YEAR BEFORE THE AGGREGATE

MR. BRUISER. MY NAME IS ANDREW COWELL.

ON BEHALF OF THE BRIDGE I'D LIKE TO WELCOME YOU TO OUR LITTLE OPERATION...

YOU READY TO SAVE THE WORLD?

I REMEMBER YOU NOW... ALWAYS TALK TALK **TALK**.

YUP... I'M STARTING TO REMEMBER MORE ABOUT **YOU** TOO...

THINGS LIKE YOUR STRICT **NO TOUCHING** RULE!

FORGIVE ME, **YOU LIVE**... I COULD HAVE TAKEN WHOLE ARM.

AH HA, NOW **THERE IS** A **BRIGHT SIDE**, WELL MATE, FORGIVE ME IF I **DON'T** SAY THANK YOU.

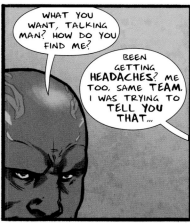

WHAT YOU WANT, TALKING MAN? HOW DO YOU FIND ME?

BEEN GETTING **HEADACHES?** ME TOO, SAME **TEAM**, I WAS TRYING TO **TELL YOU** THAT...

THAT **THING** YOU'VE BEEN SEEING IN YOUR BRAIN, THAT PRETTY PICTURE YOU **PAINTED** ON THE DECK UP TOP...

IT'S LIKE A GPS, I **PUT IT** THERE, SO WE CAN ALWAYS **FIND** EACHOTHER.

WE'RE GETTING THE **BAND** BACK TOGETHER, THIS IS **OUR** WORLD NOW...

YOU CAN **FLOAT AROUND** OUT HERE LIKE A **BLIND MULLET** FOR THE REST OF YOUR DAYS, IF THAT'S WHAT YOU WANT, OR YOU CAN **FINISH** WHAT **WE** STARTED...

SAVE THE WORLD.

SAVE THE WORLD...

LISTEN BRUISER, I'LL BE STRAIGHT WITH YOU, YOU **NEED ME** AS MUCH AS I **NEED YOU.** THE PLAN DOESN'T WORK WITHOUT **ALL 5** OF US.

BUT I'LL TELL YOU WHAT, MATE.... IF YOU'RE NOT AT THE TOP EVENTUALLY SOMEONE ELSE WILL BE, AND WHERE DO YOU THINK THAT LEAVES A BIG **MEAT AXE** LIKE YOU?

I'LL TELL YOU WHERE... RIGHT BACK WHERE YOU STARTED, IN A **CAGE** SOMEWHERE RIPPIN' OFF PEOPLE'S LIMBS.

I GAVE YOU A SECOND CHANCE ONCE....

I'M HERE TO TELL YOU THE OFFER IS STILL ON THE TABLE.

HOW'S HE HOLDING UP?

NO, NOT
AGAIN...

I'M NOT
LOSING HER
AGAIN!

SIR!

NO!

RADEK!

LET
THEM GO!

BOSS!

WHAT?!

THINK YOU COULD GIVE US A HAND?!

VALERIUS...

THE BRIDGE CALLS IT **THE AGGREGATE.**

IT'S TRUE...

THEY'RE GOING TO WIPE THE SLATE CLEAN...

90% OF THE POPULATION GONE.

LESS MOUTHS T FEED.

90%, THAT'S ALMOST EVERYBODY.

VERY GOOD.

SURVIVAL OF THE RICHEST.

I DON'T THINK WE HAVE TO TELL YOU THAT THE WORLD'S RUNNING OUT OF JUST ABOUT EVERYTHING.

PEOPLE HAVE BEEN DIGGING AND DRILLING THIS PLANE TO PIECES LOOKING FOR WHATEVER'S LEFT...

THERE'S NOTHING LEFT.

TAKE A LOOK OUTSIDE, THE AIR IS BARELY BREATHABLE IT LITERALLY RAINS **FILTH...**

THE BRIDGE KNOWS THE WORLD **CAN'T** SUSTAIN THIS, THERE'S TOO MANY OF US...

SO WHAT'S **YOUR** PLAY THEN...

IF THERE'S NOTHING LEFT TO LIVE OFF WE'RE ALL **DOOMED** ANYWAY, RIGHT?

WHEN I WAS AT THE BRIDGE, I WAS WORKING ON A SOLUTION...

I HAD IT...

IF WE CAN **STOP THE AGGREGATE,** I MIGHT BE ABLE TO--

MIGHT?

HE **CAN DO** IT...

THE BRIDGE IS DESPERATE... THEY HAVE THE MEANS TO HIT THE RESET BUTTON, YOU BETT BELIEVE THAT'S WHAT THEY'LL DO.

TO BE CONTINUED...

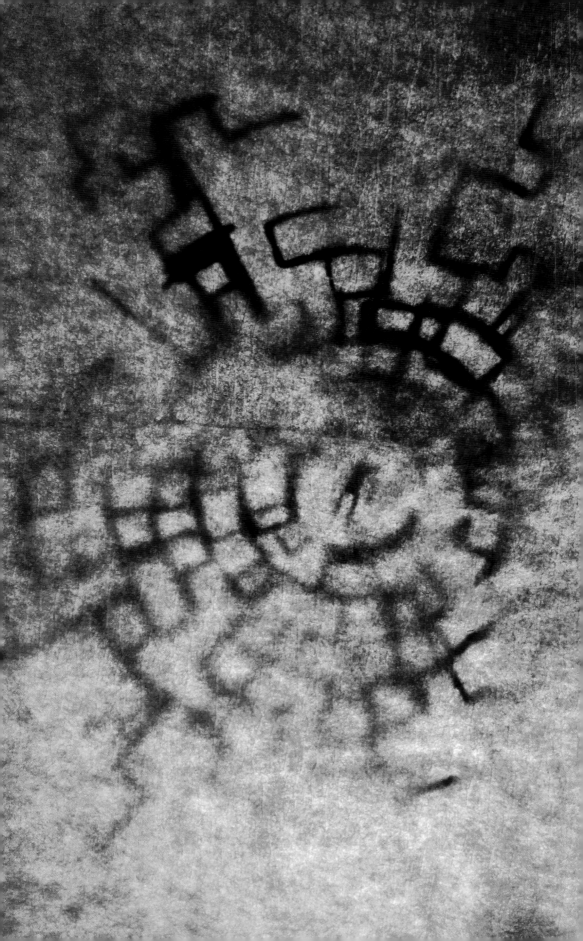

SOMETHING BOTHERING YOU SOLDIER?

HOW IS HE DOING?

NO SIR...

ARIC? AS GOOD AS CAN BE EXPECTED, I SUPPOSE...

YOU HAVE NOTHING TO FEEL GUILTY FOR...

THE OTA NEEDED TO BE STOPPED, YOU KNOW THAT...

YES, SIR.

WE ALL MAKE SACRIFICES, THE NEEDS OF THE MANY AND ALL THAT.

ARIC AND HIS BOY ARE STILL ALIVE BECAUSE OF THOSE SACRIFICES MUELLER.

WHETHER THEY KNOW THAT OR NOT... THEY HAVE PURPOSE NOW.

WE ALL DO...

AND SOON WE WILL RETURN HOME, AND THINGS WILL FALL BACK INTO PLACE. WE WILL HAVE FULL CONTROL OVER OUR OWN LIVES, FOR THE FIRST TIME.

A BRIGHTER FUTURE...

THANKS TO YOU AND THE SACRIFICES YOU HAVE MADE FOR US ALL.

NOW, CAN WE GO?

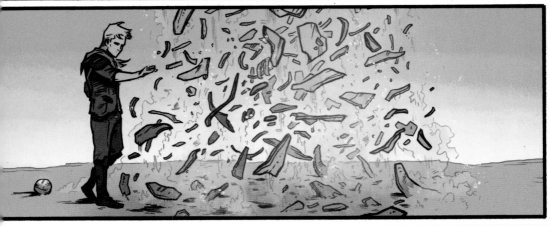

TURN TO - PAGE **184**

183

YOU WERE THE ONE WHO THREW ME OVER YOUR SHOULDER,

YOU TOOK ME ON YOUR LITTLE ADVENTURE!

YOU WERE THE ONE WHO JUMPED DOWN THAT PIT AFTER ME, KILLED THAT FERAL CAT...

AND SAVED MY LIFE,

YOU DIDN'T NEED MY HELP TO TELL YOU WHAT KIND OF PERSON YOU WERE THEN...

NOW YOU ASK ME IF I TRUST YOU?

AT FIRST I THOUGHT MAYBE... YOU WOKE UP JUST LIKE THE REST OF THEM, BUT YOU STARTED TO MAKE A LIFE FOR YOURSELF, BUILT A HOUSE, TOOK IN A DOG, AND AS FAR AS I KNOW YOU HAVEN'T KILLED ANYBODY YET...

oof!

BUT THEN YOU STARTED WALKING... SAME AS THEM, I KNEW I COULDN'T STOP YOU...

ALL I COULD DO WAS HOPE WHEN YOU GOT HERE I WOULDN'T REGRET NOT STICKING A KNIFE THROUGH YOUR HEART WHEN I HAD THE CHANCE,

BUT I DECIDED TO KEEP TRYING...

I HOPE YOU'LL DO THE SAME.

PIN-UPS

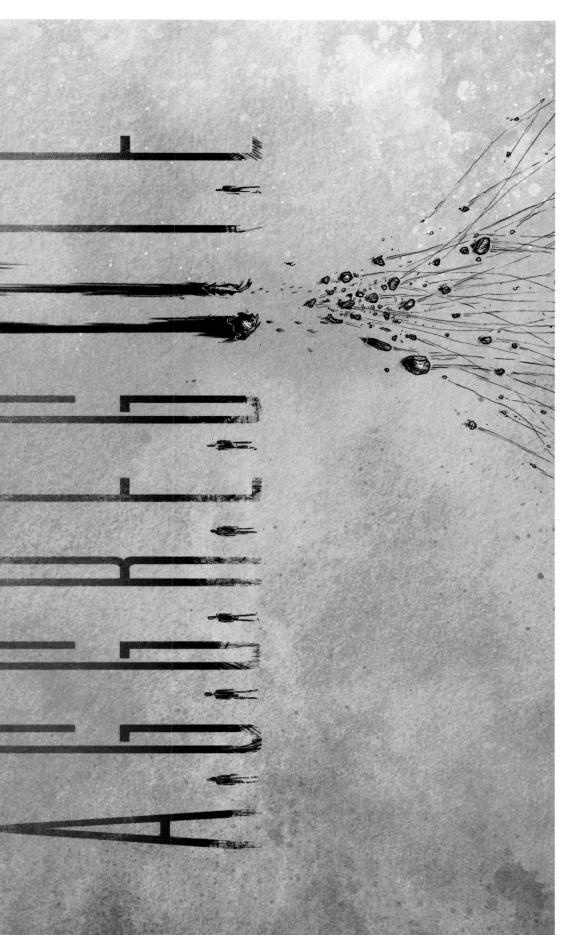

A.G.G.R.E.G.A.T.E

CHRIS DIBARI

KRISTIAN DONALDSON

RYAN LAMUNYON

A.G.G.R.E.G.I.T.E

PERRY PARKER

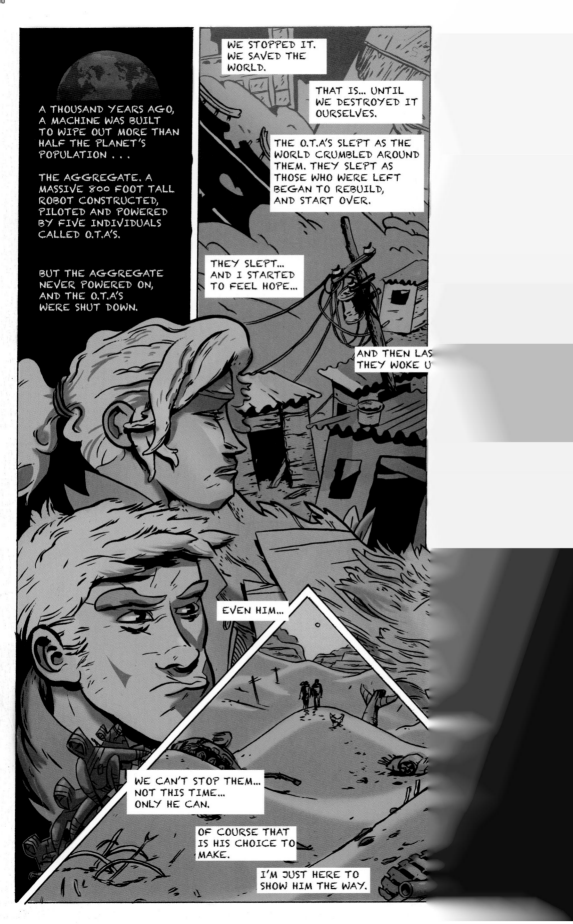

A THOUSAND YEARS AGO, A MACHINE WAS BUILT TO WIPE OUT MORE THAN HALF THE PLANET'S POPULATION . . .

THE AGGREGATE. A MASSIVE 800 FOOT TALL ROBOT CONSTRUCTED, PILOTED AND POWERED BY FIVE INDIVIDUALS CALLED O.T.A'S.

BUT THE AGGREGATE NEVER POWERED ON, AND THE O.T.A'S WERE SHUT DOWN.

WE STOPPED IT. WE SAVED THE WORLD.

THAT IS... UNTIL WE DESTROYED IT OURSELVES.

THE O.T.A'S SLEPT AS THE WORLD CRUMBLED AROUND THEM. THEY SLEPT AS THOSE WHO WERE LEFT BEGAN TO REBUILD, AND START OVER.

THEY SLEPT... AND I STARTED TO FEEL HOPE...

AND THEN LAS[...] THEY WOKE U[...]

EVEN HIM...

WE CAN'T STOP THEM... NOT THIS TIME... ONLY HE CAN.

OF COURSE THAT IS HIS CHOICE TO MAKE.

I'M JUST HERE TO SHOW HIM THE WAY.

FIDEL MURILLO

RYAN WING

RYAN WING

THANK YOU TO EVERYONE WHO SUPPORTED THIS BOOK THROUGH

KICKSTARTER

SERRA WALLERIUS - PAT LAMMERS - RYAN WING - DAN FLEMING - JOSH RUSSELL - CLINT BENSON - PATRICK COUHIE -
JOHN MACLEOD - THE VAN WESTS - STEVE - ANDREW E. C. HEAD - FLIX JACOB - JOSH ATKINSON - MARY COHEN -
LAS WARREN - ROSHAUN HESLIN - AIDAN LOGUIDICE - AL BILLINGS - TASHA ROSENBAUM - CHARLES YANG - ANDRS ALZATE - AMIE KEY -
NY SAVAGE - OLTHAR - LORA - JOSEPH ROCHELEAU - MAEGHAN MCCOID - JACOB E. WEICHERT - KENNETH LIVITSKI - JARED FLYNN KENNE-
GENEVIEVE MORGAN - S.C.V. TAYLOR - CHRIS ROSS - ZACH VAN STANLEY - SRGIO PEREIRA - DEREK PINEAPPLE STEAK SWOYER - SARAH
ARLE - TORO - ALYSSA CROW - ANDREW REAVES - THATRAJA - JEFF WAMESTER - DAN LARSON - MIKE & JEN VANCE - STEVEN
HARA - TAYLOR BIG PAPPI SPENCER - DANNY RUTA - KRIS LACHOWSKI - MARKUS AURELIUS - ASHLEIGH BAHAM - KARA MCGINTY - SAMUEL
LAS MILLER - CELESTE X. A. REIGN - ALEXANDER GUDDHA GUDENAU - JOSH HAROLD - RUKESH PATEL (LALLIPOLAZA) - AGUSTINUS AP
REMY BROWN - KENNY WONG - BRENTON BARNES - FREDRIK HOLMQVIST - CHAN CUPCAKE GHATAORE - DAMJAN MILADINOVIC - KITSUNE
OR - DAVID CECHINI - SHAWN FRENCH - DAN SCHOENING - SAMUEL LARKIN - MIKE VANCE-JRMY BARBARE NOY-ZACK NOLIN-ROMAN-KRIS-
NILSEN-SCOTT BEVERIDGE-SAMUEL HORTON - DAVID ARINGTON- HAFIZ ZAIN THE DRAGON SLAYER - HARRY MARTIN - LIZ HELLER - MACHO
RANDY SAVAGE - JOSHUA BODWELL - SKYE PRIESTLEY - THE VIRUETS - SHIREEN SHAHAWY - JAMISON MCLEAN - MICHAEL SHUGARS - KIM
NSKI - CHRIS MOREY - BRANDON THOMAS - MICHAEL ALLEN ROSE - TAYLOR HENLEY-JESTER - BRIAN LYNCH - TYRUS VON DOOM - JOSH
ILLO - ELIZABETH SIEGEL - AYALA SOROTSKY - JACOB, ANDREW, - VIOLET CORCORAN - AUSTIN FREER - OUR HERO ANDY - SARAH
BETH CAMP - EISABESS CHEE THE UNICORN WHISPERER - LEE FRENCH - ANDREW CHRISTMAN - LEE BARNES - JENNY EVERETT - DE-
THU MAKOWSKI - GARTH SUTTON - CALEB G COTE - SEAN WALSH - CARRIE CLIPS MCCLAIN - R.T. BRYSON - JIM BURZELK - JON
EY HUFF - MIKE GORMAN - ZEN SAYER - TOM DRAKE - WILLIAM DIKES - SANTIAGO BW - PETE PAGUYO - ALEX SAMARA - COMICGUY
SEPH MCDERMOTT - KEL - BLAKE BROWN - MASCARA KABOOM - JENNIFER MORRISON - ANDREW CONNEELY - ELLEN GALES - OSJUA
ON - RATT - COLLEEN - DAVID BENEVIDES - JOVANZIE - VINCE BELLOWS - MIKE BARBER - SEAN MAC G - WOLFGANG MLLER - ARIN
ALL - DENNYS ANTUNISH - DEVON CAMEL - RICHARD BAG - SKYLAR PATRIDGE - NICK W - SAMANTHA BORING - PETE KILPATRICK - D.M.
LES - TAMMY MCCRACKEN - JAMES HAICK - ANH-THU DO - DAMIEN SCOTT-SIMONS - KENDALL BULLEN - RACHAEL SMITH - AARON
BERRY - JUDY PAOLINI - MJ SHARKEY - CHADVENTURE - TONY MALAAB - CARTER - MICHELLE - NO THANKS - MICKEY HALL - RAMEL
ETMAN HILL - BRANDON N. - PETER BENSLEY - JIM NEWMAN - VEN WILSON - MATT KEITH - BRANDON MICHAEL BARKER - JUAN
OYERVIDES JR - TEO KOK SIONG - BRYAN K BORGMAN (AKA STRATOS) - BRIAN WILK - ELISE M. GROSS - DEVON R. WHALEN - ETHAN
ERON - DEVEARLEY - J. ROSS - CHLO DUDA - PYKE VAN ZON - A. DAVID LEWIS - MARJORIE G. GALLANT - MICHAEL HOWE - INDIGO
MAN - GISELLE LAFRANCE - KITTY EAST - ROLO - ELIZABETH NEEF - JASON CRASE - LYN SMITH - RAUL A. RODRIGUEZ - JULIA G
- SEAN CLOSSON - RKH BERNATOVECH - CHRIS BROWN - ROBBIE WALLIS - TREVOR PRICE - JEFF LANNING - EMILY SWAN - CAITLIN
K - GREG TAUSCH - STEVE LORD - SAMANTHA DURKIN - TEVIN HILL - DANNY KRIEGBAUM LAURSEN - ISAAC WILL IT WORK DANSICKER
SIAH & JESSICA A. - DANIELLE LEBLANC - MIHAELA MIHAILOVA - ALEJO SOTO - D. GAARDER - JENNIFER V - CAMERON LOOS - JOSH
'S - ANDY SMITH - ANONYMOUS - MYTHWIT-MIKE - TYSON PEASE - SETH CROFTON - BRETT P. HOYER - AARON HUGHES - LAURA
RS - CLARA NOHLEN - RONALD J. CURELL - GREG PAK - MIKE GARLEY - ERIK BITMANIS - RYAN PORTER - CHRIS ARTIGA-OLIVER -
"JAN WALAARDT - IAN HOPKINS KANE - NICOLE & JASON CORRY - MARQUISTADOR - AYANNI HANNA - ROBERT J GUADAGNO - YURI
CRANER - GIBRAN GRAHAM - BEN TARGETT - JARED PHILLIPS - TY GOWEN - RYAN QUINT - LAMONT BASE MASSEY -
MARTYPARTY - GATO - KURT ROSCILLO - RAYMOND HAUGLAND CRAZY NORWEGIAN - LEO A. JENSEN - PAUL R. SCHWARBER - ADAM
MAN - THE GUNDERMANS - TYMOTHY PETER DIAZ - CURTIS LINE - CHRIS ABRAM - MARTIN CHUNG - STACEY SHERMAN - ROB PAQUET
N NAGASAKO - PANG PEOW YEONG & FAMILY - MICHAEL JACKSON KIRBY - PETER BRUSH - DWAYNE STEWART - RAYSHAN - ERIK
EN - JEFFREY J. ELLEN - MARK SPAHR - SUZI SADLER - MICHAEL LEAL - ROB RYAN - XAVIER J LETT - COLE SORENSEN - LUKE
TZUOO - CHASE SHIEL - EVAN PITSTICK - ADAM THOMPSON - JAROSLAW ESYMONT - TERESA - GEORGE RUBIO - ADAM WISE - ZACH
S - MACKENZIE THE MAGNIFICENT - JEN PROPST - ALVIN SCHULTZ - ADAM SIETING - DAVID WATKINS - JACK STOLZ - JOSEPH SCHMALKE
NICHOLAS POONAMALLEE - MATTHEW WILLIAM KAYAL - KAYLA HALLEUR - JAMES LARKE - JOE MARTINO - ALEXANDER GATES - DAVID A
NA - ADAM CARPARELLI - JOHN FORD - BENJAMIN PISCOPO - SARAH E. PFEFFER - BEN TEMPLESMITH - DAVE - ENZO GARZA - ZEBAK
FANG - MEGAN MANN - TRENT HILL - KARL OKERHOLM - WILLIAM - VIET BOLO HUYNH - PETER CUNNINGHAM - MORGAN ROSENBLUM
TYPHOIS - JOEL DESMOND - MILAN KOVACS - DREW COOLEY - STEPHANIE LAY - ADAM REYES - IOANNES PATREM - RYAN - DAVID
R - ALBERT LOUIS PRICE - NICK MACARI - JAY LIBBY - MAX PFEFFER - BILLY MAHONEY - JOHN J OSTROSKY JR - MIKE - BRIAN
KOB RYOKU WALKER - LEO AQUINO - LYTTLETON L CALLENDER - CHRISTOPHER TA - TRACY TIMMONS - WOLFXTEN - BENJAMIN C.
CINDY - LAURA MUSOLF - DEVON COFFIN - RYAN H. JACKSON - GERRY A FOSTER - EVAN LIMBERGER - CETHY - MARK HIRSCHMAN -
DONOVAN-LANDIS - AIDEN - SIM PAGE - GEOFF MARTIN - LARISSA COOK - LINDA BOUDREAU - MICHAEL CALLAN - FORREST - FRAZER
EY - PETER BRYANT - ADRI - PATRICK SANTAGAPITA - STEPHANIE COFRIN - MICHAEL THOMAS O'KELLY JR - PERRY PARKER - RYAN
STA-MCKENZIE - ZACH GOHL - KYLE BUCKINGHAM - SUE PALMER - DREW HARMON - A. WANING - BRENNAN DILL - NICHOLAS PATRIZIO
HARD E. GROPP - ANTONY T CURTIS - ANDREW LEE - KERI A - DANI DEYONG - MEMPHIS - JEREMY DUNN - SOKHEAN JONATHAN OUK
TORIUS MICHEL REMAK - JOHN FISHER - ROBERT EARLY - NICOLAS NOBLE - JACK GRZYBALA - BON ALIMAGNO - JUSTIN COVERT
DREW COWELL - LEE COSTA - ARI SHAPIRO - THOMAS MUELLER - CARLA KEENAN - ERIC DALE RYAN - PEDRO MIGUEL
JES BENTO - LINDA LACKEY - JIM GREENE - CONNOR BARRETT - JIM KEENAN - JARROD RANDEL - R~ - JOSHUA VAN PELT -
PETERSON - KELLI MEATTEY - TREVOR - KEVLAUR HD KWONG - SETH MORRIS - DIMAS - BEN - NIKKI SRISOOTI - FRAN SHUM - VAN
ME - GRAYSON TIBERIUS MCGHEE - JOHNATHAN LYON - LUKE KEPPLER - DON, BETH & MEGHAN FERRIS - MATTHEW KENNETH BEDNARICK
RRY D. BARNHILL JR. - CTRLALTFACEROLL - SHAUGI SALMI - JAKE COTE - DANNY A. RUSSELL - CAITLIN HUGHES - FIDEL THE RATTLE
E MURILLO - JOSH ATKINS - AIMEE LARUE HALEY - MARTIN HOAG - SAMUEL HORTON - GREG TURPIN - DR. CHRISTOPHER RANDEL - R.
JOS FRAGA - ARTHUR VON ESCHEN - TRAVIS ELLISOR - ANGELINE BURTON - ROSS KEARNEY - A.L.HUNT - ASH -
SHEEHAN - JUSTIN OLMSTEAD - LISA EPSTEIN - ROSS HOPKINS - SETH LOUEY - COLIN EPSTEIN - RYAN GALLAGHER - TED BIASELLI
JOULE LEE - BRENDA MACLELLAN - BOB MACLELLAN - BLAKE MACLELLAN - JACK BISHOP - JILL BISHOP - EVE BISHOP -
BRAD BISHOP JR - BRADLEY BISHOP- JILL LOPEZ BISHOP

SPECIAL THANKS

EXECUTIVE PRODUCERS PAT LAMMERS, OLIVER SMITH, GERALD VON STODDARD & MARCELA PERES...
PRODUCTION ASSISTANTS JESENIA SANTANA & CODY GAUTHIER...
COLOR FLATTER MICHAEL ANGELO ARBON FLATTING ASSISTANCE DOUGLAS SHOVAR...
SOUNDTRACK TAYLOR PARNELL... KS VIDEO JOEL DESMOND...
EDITING ASSISTANCE RYAN WING & JOSEPH SCHMALKE... COLORIST BRITTANY PEER...
AND YOU!

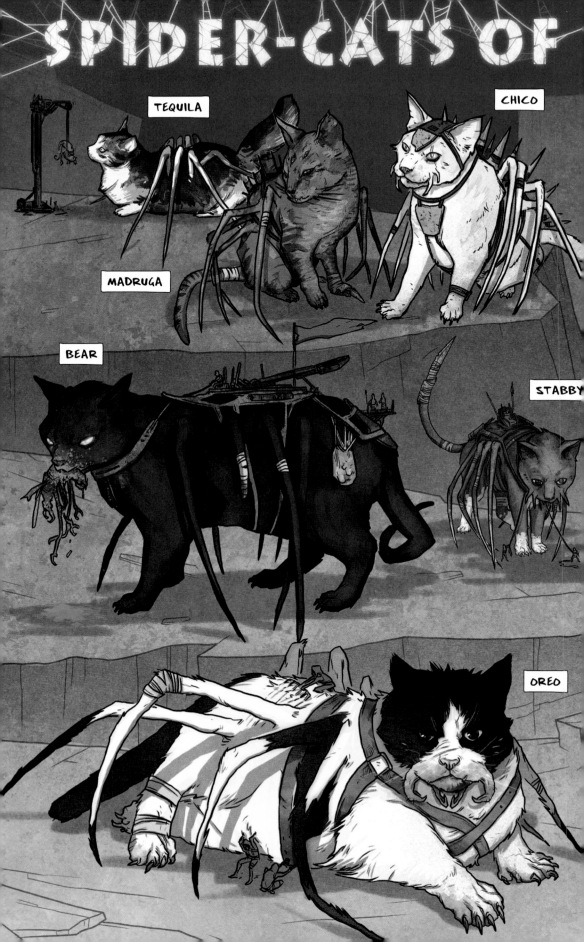

ASSEMBLING THE

A.G.G.R.E.G.I.T.E

BEHIND THE SCENES SKETCHBOOK

WAY BACK IN 2009 MY BROTHER AND I WERE KICKIN
AROUND IDEAS ABOUT A POST APOCALYPTIC COMIC W
WANTED TO WORK ON TOGETHER... HE HAD BEEN WATC
AN UNHEALTHY AMOUNT OF **LIFE AFTER PEOPLE** ON
HISTORY CHANNEL AND THEY SAID SOMETHING ABOUT H
IN THE FUTURE WITHOUT PEOPLE CREATURES LIKE SPID
OR SCORPIONS COULD GROW TO THE SIZE OF BOWLI
BALLS, AND THAT CATS WOULD LIVE UP IN SKYSCRAPE
AND EVOLVE TO GLIDE DOWN LIKE FLYING SQUIRRELS.
CAN SEE HOW I LATER COMBINED THOSE 2 IDEAS INT
WHAT WOULD EVENTUALLY BECOME THE **SPIDER-CAT**

THIS PIECE HERE I DREW FOR MY BROTHER FOR XMAS WAS AS FAR AS OUR STORY TOGETHER WENT,
WE GOT TOO CAUGHT UP IN THE SCIENCE OF WHAT THE WORLD WOULD **ACTUALLY** BE LIKE 1000 YEARS
FROM NOW. 6 YEARS LATER, WHEN I BEGAN THINKING ABOUT **THE AGGREGATE**, I LET THE STORY SHAPE
ITSELF BASED **FIRST** ON WHATEVER I THOUGHT WOULD BE COOL TO DRAW - AND **SECOND** ON THE
SCIENCE BEHIND **WHY** IT ACTUALLY EXISTED IN THIS WORLD...

FOR ALL WE HAVE AND ARE, FOR ALL OUR CHILDREN'S FATE, STAND UP AND TAKE THE WAR, THE HUN IS AT THE GATE! OUR WORLD HAS PASSED AWAY, IN WANTONNESS O'ERTHROWN. THERE IS NOTHING LEFT TO-DAY BUT STEEL AND FIRE AND STONE! THOUGH ALL WE KNEW DEPART, THE OLD COMMANDMENTS STAND: "IN COURAGE KEPT YOUR HEART, IN STRENGTH LIFT UP YOUR HAND."

"OR ALL WE HAVE AND ARE" BY RUDYARD KIPLING 1914

IT'S PRETTY COOL TO COMPARE THESE EARLY SKETCHES WITH THE MAN, NOTING THE LITTLE THINGS THAT STAYED IN HIS DESIGN. THINGS LIKE THE SINGLE SHOULDER PAD, THE JACKET, THE CAPE...

I DON'T REMEMBER THE STORY BEHIND THESE GOONS, BUT I CAN DEFINITELY SEE SOME BRUISER BEGINNINGS IN THAT BIG GUY...

ALSO I'M NOW REALIZING I USED THE WHOLE BOARD WITH NAILS IN IT THING ON THE BOILERS IN THIS BOOK.

THE VILLAIN HAD SCORPION GLOVES AND WAS OF COURSE DISFIGURED. THAT SPIKE ON HIS BOOT REMINDS ME A LOT OF A LIGHT SOLDIER'S SHOULDER DESIGN!

WHEN THE MAN BECAME **THE MAN**... WHEN I STARTED SOLIDIFYING **THE MAN**'S DESIGN I KNEW I WANTED TO STRAY A BIT FROM THE DARK HAIRED LEADING MAN I HAD CAST IN SOME OF MY PREVIOUS BOOKS, SO I STARTED PLAYING WITH A SUN DRENCHED BEACH BLONDE LOOK AND THOUGHT IT LOOKED PRETTY GOOD. LATER I READ A NATIONAL GEOGRAPHIC ARTICLE THAT DEDUCED HOW HUMANS WOULD LOOK IN THE FUTURE AND IT WAS PRETTY SPOT ON TO HOW I WAS PUTTING TOGETHER **VALERIUS** AND **THE MAN**, SO IT WORKED OUT.

THE ORIGINS OF THE **SPIDER-CATS**.... I KNEW I WANTED CATS IN THE BOOK, BUT HONESTLY HAD NO IDEA WHY, AND I'M GLAD I STUCK TO IT BECAUSE THE CATS WERE LIKE INTERNET GOLD WHEN I DECIDED TO DO A **KICKSTARTER**, PEOPLE FREAKIN' LOVE CATS. ANYWAY, INITIALLY THEY WERE JUST BIG AND GROSS.... THEN I MIXED THEM WITH THE GIANT SCORPIONS, THEN THE SCORPIONS TURNED TO SPIDERS AND THEN... WELL THE REST IS HISTORY.

MORE **VALERIUS**... I REALLY DID FALL IN LOVE WITH THIS CHARACTER. I LOVE HER ARC FROM WHO SHE IS IN THE BEGINNING OF THE BOOK TO WHAT SHE BECOMES AS THE TIME GOES ON... AND ON... AND ON... HER HAIR WAS A LOT OF FUN. THERE WERE A FEW TIMES WHERE I WOULD FORGET WHAT SIDE WAS SHAVED THOUGH AND HAD TO LOOK BACK.

VALERIUS WAS COMING RIGHT FROM **THE LIGHT** IN THE STORY, BUT ALSO NEEDED HER OWN LOOK TO DIFFERENCIATE HERSELF FROM THEM. BRITTANY WAS SMART TO KEEP HER IN PURPLE FROM THE START. SHE MIGHT BE WITH **THE LIGHT**, BUT SHE'S GOING TO DRESS HOWEVER THE HELL SHE WANTS TO.

...RE ARE A COUPLE UNUSED ...AGES YOU MAY HAVE SEEN ...N THE **KICKSTARTER.** I ...LVAGED A COUPLE PANELS ...ND FACES THAT YOU CAN ...T FOR IN THE BOOK, BUT ...RALL THE QUALITY OF THEM ...SN'T UP TO SNUFF BECAUSE ...EY WERE A COUPLE YEARS ... BY THE TIME I ACTUALLY ...ARTED DRAWING THE FULL ...OK, THERE WASN'T A WHOLE ...T OF STORY FIGURED OUT ... BE HONEST, I GAVE **RADEK** ... MESSED UP HAND BECAUSE ...LAINS ARE ALWAYS LOSING ...Y PARTS... IT WASN'T UNTIL ...ATER THAT I DECIDED TO ...ITE A SCENE SHOWING **HOW** ...HAT ACTUALLY HAPPENED.

THIS WAS ORIGINALLY THE SCENE WHERE **RADEK** IS BEING TOLD THAT **THE MAN** WAS ON THE RUN, CUT WITH **VALERIUS** CHECKING OUT THE MAP ON THE FLOOR OF HIS SHACK. YOU MAY HAVE NOTICED THE MAP HAS BEEN CHANGED. A LOT OF THOUGHT WENT BEHIND THE NEW MAP AND I CAN'T SPOIL TOO MUCH NOW SO I'LL JUST SHUT UP... BUT SOME COOL REVEALS ARE COMING IN BOOK 2 AS FAR AS THE MAP TO **THE AGGREGATE** IS CONCERNED.

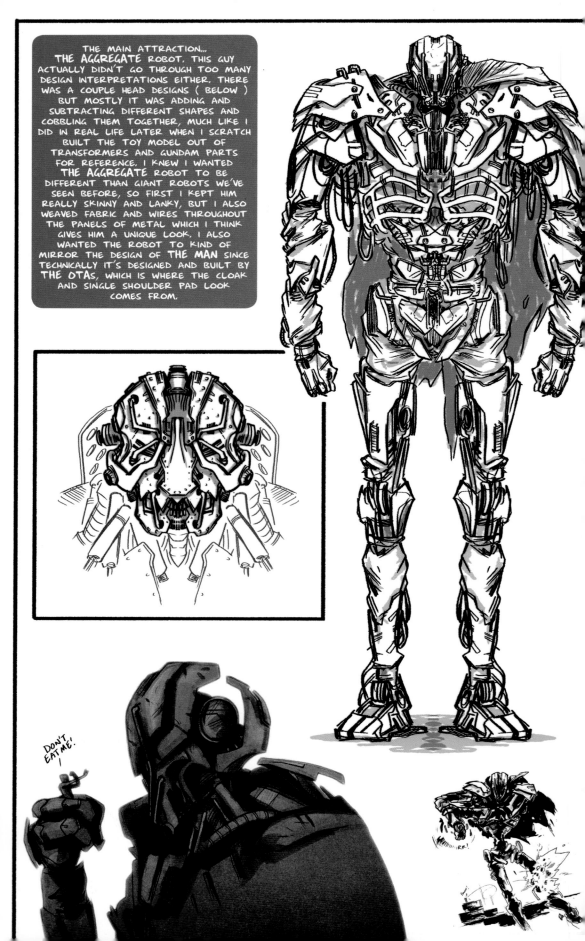

THE MAIN ATTRACTION...
THE AGGREGATE ROBOT. THIS GUY ACTUALLY DIDN'T GO THROUGH TOO MANY DESIGN INTERPRETATIONS EITHER. THERE WAS A COUPLE HEAD DESIGNS (BELOW) BUT MOSTLY IT WAS ADDING AND SUBTRACTING DIFFERENT SHAPES AND COBBLING THEM TOGETHER, MUCH LIKE I DID IN REAL LIFE LATER WHEN I SCRATCH BUILT THE TOY MODEL OUT OF TRANSFORMERS AND GUNDAM PARTS FOR REFERENCE. I KNEW I WANTED **THE AGGREGATE** ROBOT TO BE DIFFERENT THAN GIANT ROBOTS WE'VE SEEN BEFORE, SO FIRST I KEPT HIM REALLY SKINNY AND LANKY, BUT I ALSO WEAVED FABRIC AND WIRES THROUGHOUT THE PANELS OF METAL WHICH I THINK GIVES HIM A UNIQUE LOOK. I ALSO WANTED THE ROBOT TO KIND OF MIRROR THE DESIGN OF **THE MAN** SINCE TECHNICALLY IT'S DESIGNED AND BUILT BY **THE OTAs**, WHICH IS WHERE THE CLOAK AND SINGLE SHOULDER PAD LOOK COMES FROM.

DON'T EAT ME!

THE BIG DEPARTING THOUGHT THAT TOOK ME FROM THE IDEA WITH MY BROTHER TO WHAT IT IS NOW IS REALLY THE **ROBOT**. I WAS THINKING ABOUT POWER RANGERS AND VOLTRON AND EVANGELION AND ROBOTECH AND... YOU GET IT... AND I THOUGHT, "OK, BUT WHY ARE **THOSE KIDS** THE POWER RANGERS?" JUST BECAUSE THEY ARE ALL FRIENDS AND WEAR BRIGHT COLORS? I WANTED TO FIND AN EXPLANATION FOR THE INDIVIUALS AND HOW THEIR POWERS WORKED AND **WHY** THEY WOULD NEED A **GIANT** ROBOT THAT THEY ALL USE TOGETHER WHEN THEY ALL ALREADY HAVE THEIR OWN **MEDIUM** ROBOTS... AND WHAT HAPPENS IF THEY DON'T ALL AGREE TO USE IT?

HERE IS MY BELOVED CAST OF **AGGREGATE ACTORS**. THESE ARE ALL **REAL PEOPLE** THAT CHOSE
KICKSTARTER REWARD TO BE IN THE BOOK. YOU'LL BE SEEING A LOT MORE FROM THEM IN BO[OK]
2 AS WELL... NONE OF THEM HAVE BEEN KILLED OFF... **YET!** IT WAS DEFINITELY A CHALLENGE TO [FIT]
THESE PEOPLE INTO THE STORY AND **THE AGGREGATE** WORLD. I FOUND IT HELPFUL AND FUN TO [PLAY]
OFF OF ASPECTS OF THEIR REAL LIVES AND PUT THAT INTO THEIR CHARACTER. FOR EXAMPLE, MZ[.K]
IS ACTUALLY A TEACHER IN REAL LIFE SO I MADE HER A TRAINER IN THE BOOK. **COVERT** WAS IN [THE]
MILITARY, SO HIS CHARACTER WAS TOO. **LEE** IS A GUN NUT, SO... **LEE** IS A GUN NUT IN THE BOO[K]

THE LIGHT ARE BASICALLY A BUNCH OF NINJA MONKS, SO THAT'S WHERE THE DESIGN STARTS AND ENDS. THEY ARE REALLY FUN TO DRAW.

I HAD COME UP WITH THE SHOULDER SPIKE DESIGN BEFORE I EVEN KNEW WHY. LATER IT WORKED OUT WITH THE STORY THAT THE STONE REFLECTS MOONLIGHT WHICH WOULD DISORIENT WHOEVER THEY WERE FIGHTING – WHICH THEN OF COURSE ALSO WORKED OUT WITH THEIR NAME, THE LIGHT. FASHION-ABLE **AND** FUNCTIONABLE... PROBABLY WHY VAL STILL HASN'T DROPPED IT FROM HER OUTFIT.

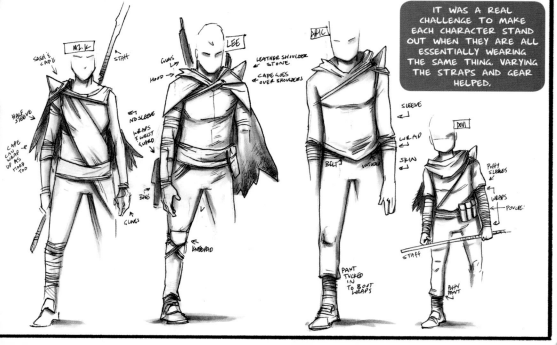

IT WAS A REAL CHALLENGE TO MAKE EACH CHARACTER STAND OUT WHEN THEY ARE ALL ESSENTIALLY WEARING THE SAME THING. VARYING THE STRAPS AND GEAR HELPED.

MZ. K

SASH & CAPE
STAFF
HALF SLEEVE
CAPE CAN WRAP UP AS HOOD TOO
GLOVES

LEE

GUNS
HOOD
NO SLEEVE
WRAPS & WRIST GUARD
BAGS
KNEEPAD

MAC

LEATHER SHOULDER STONE
CAPE GOES OVER SHOULDERS
BELTS UNTUCKED
PANT TUCKED IN TO BOOT WRAPS

DOVI

SLEEVE
WRAP
SKIN
PUFFY SLEEVES
WRAPS
POUCHE
STAFF
PLAIN PANT

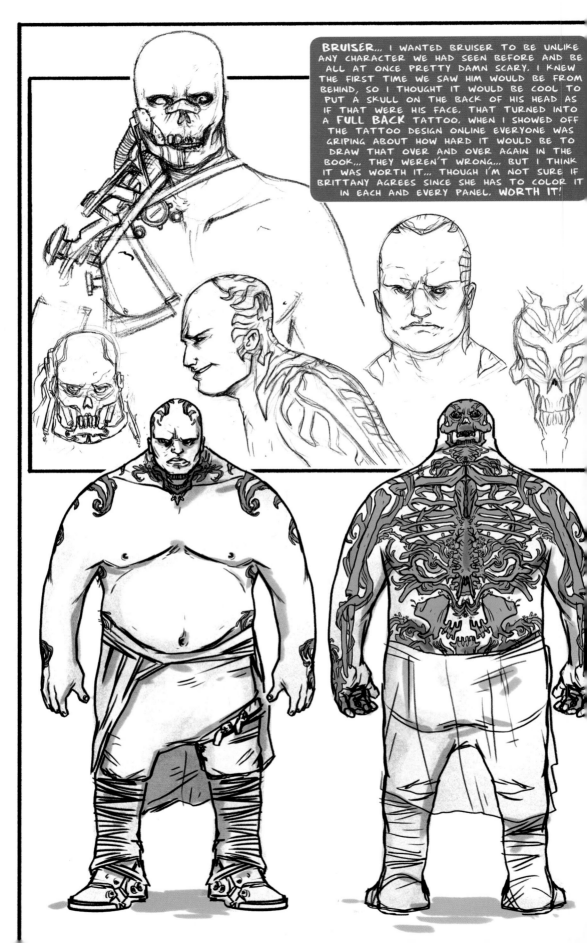

BRUISER... I WANTED BRUISER TO BE UNLIKE ANY CHARACTER WE HAD SEEN BEFORE AND BE ALL AT ONCE PRETTY DAMN SCARY, I KNEW THE FIRST TIME WE SAW HIM WOULD BE FROM BEHIND, SO I THOUGHT IT WOULD BE COOL TO PUT A SKULL ON THE BACK OF HIS HEAD AS IF THAT WERE HIS FACE, THAT TURNED INTO A **FULL BACK** TATTOO, WHEN I SHOWED OFF THE TATTOO DESIGN ONLINE EVERYONE WAS GRIPING ABOUT HOW HARD IT WOULD BE TO DRAW THAT OVER AND OVER AGAIN IN THE BOOK... THEY WEREN'T WRONG... BUT I THINK IT WAS WORTH IT... THOUGH I'M NOT SURE IF BRITTANY AGREES SINCE SHE HAS TO COLOR IT IN EACH AND EVERY PANEL. **WORTH IT!**

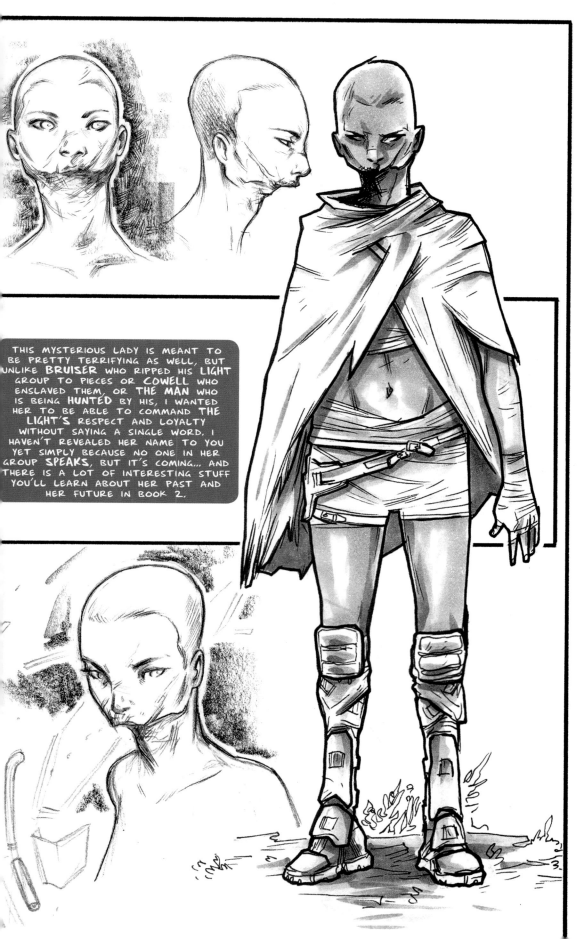

THIS MYSTERIOUS LADY IS MEANT TO BE PRETTY TERRIFYING AS WELL, BUT UNLIKE **BRUISER** WHO RIPPED HIS **LIGHT** GROUP TO PIECES OR **COWELL** WHO ENSLAVED THEM, OR **THE MAN** WHO IS BEING **HUNTED** BY HIS, I WANTED HER TO BE ABLE TO COMMAND **THE LIGHT'S** RESPECT AND LOYALTY WITHOUT SAYING A SINGLE WORD, I HAVEN'T REVEALED HER NAME TO YOU YET SIMPLY BECAUSE NO ONE IN HER GROUP **SPEAKS**, BUT IT'S COMING... AND THERE IS A LOT OF INTERESTING STUFF YOU'LL LEARN ABOUT HER PAST AND HER FUTURE IN BOOK 2.

A.G.O.R.E.G.I.T.E

BOOK 2

BEN BISHOP IS A COMIC CREATOR FROM MAINE

WHO STARTED DRAWING AT FOUR YEARS OLD AND BEGAN MAKING HIS OWN COMICS AT AGE ELEVEN.

IN 2008, HE RELEASED HIS FIRST ORIGINAL GRAPHIC NOVEL, THE 300 PAGE, NATHAN THE CAVEMAN,

IN 2011, BEN ILLUSTRATED THE AWARD-WINNING BOOK LOST TRAIL: NINE DAYS ALONE IN THE WILDERNESS, THE GRAPHIC NOVEL RETEL OF THE FAMOUS MAINE TRUE STORY, LOST ON A MOUNTAIN IN MAINE, WHICH LED TO ILLUSTRATION WORK FOR LARGER COMPANIES ARCHAIA, IDW, DARBY POP, ACTION LAB, NICKELODEON AND HASBRO. BEN ALSO JUMPED AT THE OPPORTUNITY TO CREATE COMIC CO ART FOR SOME OF HIS FAVORITE CHARACTERS LIKE BATMAN, THE TEENAGE MUTANT NINJA TURTLES, TRANSFORMERS, AND G.I.JOE

IN 2015, BEN LAUNCHED A KICKSTARTER CAMPAIGN FOR HIS NEXT BOOK, THE AGGREGATE. WITH A GOAL OF $10,000, WHICH WAS HIT IN THE FIRST 24 HOURS, THE AGGREGATE CAMPAIGN WENT ON TO RAISE 3 TIMES TH

THANKS TO THE DEMAND AND EXCITEMENT OF HIS FRIENDS, FAMILY, AND FANS, THIS BOOK YOU'RE HOLDING NOW EXISTS.

WWW.BISHART.NET (INSTAGRAM AND TWITTER) @BISHART

BRITTANY PEER IS A COLORIST

WHO SPENDS MOST OF HER FREE TIME LAYING ON THE FLOOR OF HER OFFICE WITH HER CAT OR PLAYING OVERWATCH. WHEN SHE'S BUSY COLORING GIANT SPIDER-CATS FOR THE AGGREGATE, SHE'S LENDING HER COLORS TO BOOM! STUDIOS' SLAM AND JONESY.

WWW.BRITTANYPEER.COM (TWITTER) @BR_PEER